# She Had Never Been So Affected by a Man Before . . .

and it frightened her beyond belief. Always in charge, Vicky had never thought she would be swept off her feet by a domineering male.

"You're so soft, so sweet tasting." Kurt's voice was rough, sensuous.

A torrent of emotions rushed through her as his tongue explored the warmth of her mouth. Suddenly she was responding, fully and feverishly.

Her mind whirled. She had always made fun of the girls who swore that fireworks really did happen. It had never seemed possible. Until now . . .

## *RITA CLAY*

has tried almost every job once. This former book-store manager worked in a bank, sold cosmetics, and ran her own modeling school before turning to writing. Now a successful romance author, she looks forward to describing the diversity and joys of love in many books to come.

Dear Reader:

SILHOUETTE DESIRE is an exciting new line of contemporary romances from Silhouette Books. During the past year, many Silhouette readers have written in telling us what other types of stories they'd like to read from Silhouette, and we've kept these comments and suggestions in mind in developing SILHOUETTE DESIRE.

DESIREs feature all of the elements you like to see in a romance, plus a more sensual, provocative story. So if you want to experience all the excitement, passion and joy of falling in love, then SILHOUETTE DESIRE is for you.

I hope you enjoy this book and all the wonderful stories to come from SILHOUETTE DESIRE. I'd appreciate any thoughts you'd like to share with us on new SILHOUETTE DESIRE, and I invite you to write to us at the address below:

Karen Solem
Editor-in-Chief
Silhouette Books
P.O. Box 769
New York, N.Y. 10019

# RITA CLAY
# Experiment In Love

*Silhouette Desire*

Published by Silhouette Books New York

**America's Publisher of Contemporary Romance**

**Other Silhouette Books by Rita Clay**

*Wanderer's Dream*
*Wise Folly*
*Sweet Eternity*
*Yesterday's Dreams*

 SILHOUETTE BOOKS, a Simon & Schuster Division of
GULF & WESTERN CORPORATION
1230 Avenue of the Americas, New York, N.Y. 10020

Copyright © 1983 by Rita Clay

Distributed by Pocket Books

ISBN: 0-671-44373-9

First Silhouette Books printing February, 1983

10 9 8 7 6 5 4 3 2 1

America's Publisher of Contemporary Romance

Printed in the U.S.A.

This book is for Parris Afton Bonds:

For the tragedies and triumphs,
the good times and bad times,
and all the times in between.

For late-night phone calls
and weekend powwows.

Thank you, friend.

# Experiment In Love

# 1

~eeeeeeeeeee~

It was a sunny, quiet California morning when the alarm jangled through the plush brown and cream bedroom. Kurt Morgan already stood at the window overlooking Santa Barbara harbor, ignoring the breathtaking view. He turned and quickly shut off the jangling machine, then continued his perusal of the sunrise.

He had worked hard all his life, making his magazine one of the best in the nation. He had achieved all he had set out to do. He had met the challenges of life and had won. So why was he so restless?

Time niggled at his brain, stopping him from finding peace in the scenery any longer. He walked into the bathroom for his usual stingingly cold, brisk shower.

The large bathroom was done in the same color scheme as the masculine bedroom. Shiny oatmeal-colored tiles lined the walls and floor and crisp cream monogrammed towels hung neatly on a heated rack. There was nothing sitting out on the pristine counters to show what type of man he was. Everything was neatly kept behind mirrored doors. In fact, his bathroom matched his bedroom: plain and simple in decor, yet luxurious. Everything he could possibly need or want was there.

He had been staring out the window since before dawn, watching the small sloops sailing along the coast dip and bob in the water, feeling discontent wearing at his brain. At thirty-six he felt old and tired of his regulated way of life.

Over an hour and a half later he strode into the office marked KURT MORGAN, PRESIDENT, NEWSTIME MAGAZINE, and politely growled at his secretary for the morning's first cup of coffee; she grinned and silently complied with his bidding. That should have warned him that something was up. She had always been vitriolic on the subject of waiting on him. After all, she never tired of telling him, he paid her to be his secretary, not his maid. But for the first time in six years she wasn't griping.

He glanced over his shoulder, almost missing the small barbs that usually accompanied his command. His normal routine was suddenly off-balance.

"Are you feeling well, Margie?"

"I'm fine, Mr. Morgan. And you?" She held out his steaming cup, then placed her folded hands on her more than ample stomach, waiting for. . . . What was she waiting for?

"Good. Get me the *Anderson Report* files, would you?"

Her look surprised him. She actually seemed pleased by his request. "Are you still going ahead with that project?"

10

"I've been thinking about this series for the last two weeks. Why should I stop now?" He felt the need to stretch mentally. He was tired of being behind the desk and now he had to break that routine, find the enthusiasm to begin a new project.

"Because we don't have enough evidence to do anything with?" Her voice was dry with meaning.

Kurt had been thinking of doing a series of exposé articles on a high circulation singles newspaper that carried ads intended for the eyes of lonely people. Ads hinting that they could turn into swinging, sophisticated singles just by writing to the box number of their choice. So far there had been no evidence of other, more profitable, money-making industries tied to the *Anderson Report*—other ways to meet people and make new "friends"—but Kurt's gut feeling told him to follow up anyway. There was undoubtedly something wrong with the entire setup. He just wasn't sure what it was. Yet.

"Just find the file, please," he said in a "business as usual" tone that brooked no argument.

Margie had been with him since he had first taken over the company and knew when to obey without further argument. "If that's the way you want it. . . ." Her voice trailed off as she reached for the correct file drawer.

He stood in the doorway with his back straight, his lean muscled body taut, crossing his arms. He gave a less than enthusiastic smile. "All right, Margie. Out with it. What is it I'm supposed to ask?"

She glared at him before breaking into a smile.

"You're supposed to ask me the solution to getting an inside report on the Anderson paper and I'm supposed to give it to you."

He relaxed his stance a little, placing his hands on his well-tapered hips while Margie continued to stare at him. Even at her age she could appreciate a good build and fantastic looks: dark brown hair with golden streaks; high cheekbones; deep-set golden brown eyes; a coppery California tan. Thirty-six years old and he had everything. A house on Mulholland Drive, a beach house in Santa Barbara, a cliff house in Acapulco, total control over one of the top four magazines in the country. Enough wealth to more than maintain his style of living, including his current mistress. Everything. It was a shame he had been so discontented lately.

"What's the answer to the Anderson muddle, Margie?" He might as well play the game. He needed to keep busy.

"It's very simple, boss. Answer one of the ads yourself and take a 'swinging single' out to lunch. Ask her about herself, find out why she advertised in the newspaper to get a date, what Anderson promised and all that stuff." The cat who swallowed the canary couldn't have looked more pleased with herself. She stood watching one expression after another pass over her boss' usually impassive face.

"Impossible."

"Why?"

"It's out of the question."

"Why?"

He grinned before finally answering, "The chances

are excellent that the girl would probably be either a professional or voted the ugliest girl on the block!"

"If she's the former, then you'd have what you need for your story," Margie stated calmly. "And if she's the latter, then you still have your hook. So either way you have a story, and that's what you told me you were after."

"Some choice!" he snorted, glaring at her belligerently. "I either get a prostitute or an absolute dog!"

"I'm only suggesting you take her out once or twice and try to find out why she advertised herself in a singles newspaper. You don't have to marry the girl. You could consider it an experiment."

"We'll see."

"Or you could give the story to one of the younger reporters. They'd love to sink their teeth into something like this. I don't know why you would want to do it anyway. You've got enough to do just running this magazine."

Margie's logic was as irritating as it was true, especially the part concerning the younger reporters. They *would* just love to get their hands on something like this, and it wasn't as if they couldn't do it, it was just that, once in a while, Kurt enjoyed working on a story himself. He had done it in the beginning of his career and he occasionally needed to prove to himself that he could still do just as good a job as the next man.

He turned and entered the inner office. "I'll think about it," he threw back over his shoulder.

Margie tried to keep her chuckle low. He didn't like to be told how to do a story, especially by his secretary. The man was definitely a leader . . . in all things. His only problem was that he had never found a challenge big enough or a woman smart enough to test his mettle, so he was still a playboy bachelor. And would probably remain so, if the latest girl of his choice was anything to go by, Margie thought ruefully.

She walked back to her desk and began the morning ritual of opening mail. If only he'd give her idea some thought. She glanced at her watch. If he did, he should decide to try it by noon. On a hunch Margie picked up the phone and called down to the mail room.

"Joey, run out to the nearest newspaper stand and grab one of those *Anderson Reports*, would you? And bring it straight up! The boss wants it—pronto." She chuckled as she placed the phone back on the cradle. One thing about this job, it was always different. She'd worked at *Newstime* for twenty years and no two days were ever the same.

Victoria Branden Brown chewed on the eraser end of her pencil for a full minute before she realized she had a mouth full of rubber. Her mind had been working furiously all morning. She needed a new story with which to impress the city editor of the *Los Angeles Messenger*, something that would make him beg her to work full-time instead of just on an occasional freelance story. She had decided that the *Messenger* was the perfect newspaper to support her while she pursued her fledgling career as a writer of fiction.

"While you're finishing your notes I'll just run this

over to copy," Gina, Victoria's friend and lunchmate, said, giving a big smile as she dashed out the door and disappeared around the corner.

Victoria nodded absently, her mind still on her immediate problem: how to get money on a regular basis.

Ever since that morning an idea had been buzzing around in her mind. Maybe this would be the one. . . .

She had been working as a freelancer for the past year while she secretly wrote a book, *her* book, at home. The only reason she was at the *Newstime* offices today was that she had just finished a story on the different types of privately owned vessels that sailed the Pacific coast and decided to treat Gina, who worked there, to a celebration lunch. Gina got a regular paycheck and consequently picked up most of the checks when they went out.

Victoria's article was short, sweet, to the point and not too terribly interesting. But it paid the rent and the cost of erasers. She was dying to find a good article to sink her teeth into, but those assignments usually went to the regular full-time employees, not to freelancers like herself. In fact, the regular *Newstime* staff was so efficient and well-trained that only the stories that were used as fillers or human interest were ever handed to reporters like her.

She stiffened her back, setting the pencil back down on the desk and staring straight ahead, her mind working rapidly.

What if she found an unexplored topic for an in-depth article? A great article? What if she got an inside story on the *Anderson Report?* The topic was certainly juicy enough. Swinging singles meeting other swinging singles had to be controversial, and that's what the *L. A. Messenger* liked. Food for thought and let the reader make up his own mind.

She grinned and picked up the phone. "Information? Give me the number of the *Anderson Report,* please." Her fingers beat out an impatient tattoo as she waited for the number. Wouldn't her boss be impressed!

"Anderson Report? I'd like to place an ad in the 'Male Wanted' column of next week's edition. . . ."

Her normally smooth brow was knitted in concentration by the time she replaced the receiver. Step number one was complete, but what about step number two? How could she go on a date with a man who probably thought she was easy and stay hard to get? There had to be a way to find a date through the ad and still keep herself in one piece by the end of the evening. Her mind worked furiously as she thought of and discarded several methods. Then a thought clicked and she smiled.

Of course! Why hadn't she thought of that before? She'd have to get a new outfit, and that would make a dent in her day-to-day income, but she should be able to handle it. Her contact lenses would have to go; she'd wear her glasses. That was something she hadn't done in a long time! She mentally went over her existing makeup, discarding earthtones and light colors. She'd have to be terribly drab-looking from the neck up and sexy from the waist down. That way she could scare them with her intelligence and still stir their interest with her softly rounded form. Sort of a "come-hither" virgin! Perfect!

Gina walked back into the office. "Whew! I'm glad that's finished for the day. That assignment was a real stinker. What the mayor of a small city thinks are big issues for his next campaign." She grabbed her purse. "Let's go. I'm starved."

Victoria stood and reached for her own purse, then followed her friend out of the office and down the hall. Her dark hair fell long and straight to the middle of her back as she walked with lithe, unconscious grace toward the elevator. Several men turned to give the gamine-like woman a well-deserved second look, but she never noticed.

Walking along without noticing the admiring stares that came her way was as natural to Vicky as three-piece suits were to the average go-getter executive. She was a mixture of diverse elements, completely contemporary in some ways, unbelievably innocent in others. She never walked when she felt like running, and she could not be organized. She could understand why a person would want to swim with all their clothing on, just as she could if they wanted to swim nude, but why would they spend hours worrying about how a swimsuit looked only to sit on the edge of the pool for fear of messing up a hairdo? To Victoria, it just didn't make sense. That kind of propriety was for those who wanted to miss out on the joy of living. It was also for those who had one foot in the grave and the other foot firmly planted on the guilty consciences of their youth. Only the living could make mistakes and learn from them.

It was a philosophy that had many holes, but it was hers, and that was all that mattered. Her friends overlooked her eccentricities and forgave her her sometimes Victorian ideals.

Downtown Los Angeles was, for a change, bright and sunny. No haze hung in the air, no yellow mist clung to the tops of the buildings. She hummed as she walked beside Gina. Suddenly she stopped and raked through the bottom of her purse for loose change, then retraced her steps toward the newspaper stand and the latest copy of the *Anderson Report.* She might as well see what she had just advertised herself in. . . .

". . . but your parties don't require my presence, Julie. If you wanted me there so badly you should have informed me earlier so I could have made arrangements," Kurt said coldly. "I have other plans." He sat comfortably in his executive chair, his eyes scanning the list of figures in front of him as he listened with only half of his attention to the woman on the other end of the telephone. Eventually he hung up without saying anything more and focused his complete attention on the latest financial report.

Margie peeked around the almost-closed door, sensing before seeing the scowl that brought his brows together. "Mr. Hampton's here and the 'newspaper' we discussed last week just came out with its new issue." Of all the people in the twenty-story building, she was the only one who wasn't afraid to face him in a bad mood.

"I thought I told you that I'd think about it," he bit out.

Margie shrugged. "All right. Then let me give the assignment to someone else. It's a story that ought to be done."

"We have four reporters in Washington, three reporters each in New York, Chicago and Dallas, several in every major country in the world and you're telling me we ought to do an exposé on a small, locally run singles newspaper."

Margie's brow lifted. "The *Anderson Report* just went into Houston and San Francisco and will be moving into Chicago soon. That's small?" Irony was heavy in her voice. She knew when to push and when to leave well enough alone. This was push time.

Kurt stood and straightened his tie, his eyes shooting sparks at her. "Send Mr. Hampton in, Margie," he said, ignoring her question as he waited to greet one of their biggest advertising buyers.

By the time Mr. Hampton had left Kurt was furious with himself. Throughout the entire meeting he had actually been thinking of that damn rag. He sat quietly for a few moments, then flipped the switch on the intercom that connected him with Margie's desk.

"Margie, bring in the Anderson file and the newspaper. Make sure it's a current one." His voice was clipped and efficient, his manner all business. He might as well give her idea a try. After all, if he could handle a business concern this large he could certainly handle one lonely-hearted woman looking for a little excitement in her life.

Margie's broad grin was like a beacon as she walked into her boss' inner sanctum, the newest *Anderson Report* in her hand.

"Well, Mr. Morgan, you have enough ads to choose from in this issue to keep you busy for the next month. Do you want to decide which ones would make 'the perfect date' or should I check them out for you?"

"Weed through them, Margie. Dismiss any who can't spell their own name, then delete the ones into leather or anything else out of the ordinary. I want the average types." He sounded preoccupied.

Margie grinned. "That eliminates most of them right off the bat. I thought you were trying to find the average woman who advertised in this rag, not the average woman, period."

"Just do your job, Margie," he muttered.

"I already have." She grinned smugly at his surprised look, holding out a page with four of the ads circled in black. "Now write your letters. And after that you need to buy some new clothes."

"I have enough at home, thank you."

"Oh, yes. Three-piece suits, cashmere sweaters, designer shirts and tailor-made slacks." Margie sniffed. "And just what do you think those women are going to think when they see you coming? That they've managed to hook a very wealthy one, that's what." Kurt frowned as she continued. "You want to get them to talk to you, not have them so awed they can't speak."

"My *clothes* awe women? And all this time I thought it was my charm," he teased, a twinkle in his eyes.

"And your money. Don't forget that," she cautioned, and he sobered.

"How right you are," he muttered under his breath, a vision of Julie's latest clothing bill looming in his mind.

"So give the girl a break and buy something off the rack, preferably sexy, but understated."

"Such as?" Now he was grinning.

"A nice tweed blazer, dark cords, kind of quiet-looking. You're supposed to need help meeting a woman, remember." She screwed up her face in thought. "You need to look as if you have enough money to buy good clothes but are still suffering from a lonely heart. In other words, you have to look average."

"Right. Set me a date with"—he scanned the four circled ads, scratched out two, and handed the paper back to her—"with these two women. Let's see what happens."

"Any particular night?"

"No, any night my calendar is open."

"What about Julie?"

His face clouded. "What about her? This is business, Margie. Now, get going."

She grinned despite his frown. "Yes, boss," she said demurely, swinging her arms as she walked slowly out of the office, her ample body shaking with silent laughter. Julie was obviously on her way out. Thank goodness!

Victoria checked the mirror one more time to make sure that her makeup wasn't overstated, her dress was demure enough and her glasses weren't fogged with passion. Her hair was pulled back in a long ponytail, a style that was as old as time and, she hoped, looked about as sexy as a new mop. She didn't notice the fact that it emphasized her high cheekbones and showed off her small earlobes with their tiny earrings. Or that her mouth looked sensuous with its touch of nothing but clear gloss. She doubted that her "date" would be able to see the large gray eyes behind her heavy glasses, or notice the impish grin that constantly wanted to pull up the corners of her mouth and show off her deep dimples.

Her hands were clammy. Just yesterday she had picked up the first of the letters that had come in answer to the ad. Most had been courteous, some forward and a few downright lewd. She had chosen the first and fifth letters and had written to the rest, telling them that she had found the man of her choice. If the letters continued to come in at this rate she'd be forced to get a secretary! How many lonely people were out there, for goodness' sake?

Once more she looked down at the letter from candidate number one. He said he was a real estate salesman in Orange County and had been looking "for someone like you." How could he possibly be attracted to a twenty-word ad? She had made it as brief as possible: *If you are sweet, kind and enjoy almost anything, then call on me. I'm single, under thirty, lonely and looking.*

"Oh, good grief!" she groaned, for the first time seeing her ad as others would see it. "Did I really say I enjoyed almost anything? Am I in trouble!"

Before she could think any more about the trouble she was in the doorbell rang. With a stiff upper lip and a quivering chin, Victoria marched to the door. If worse came to worse she could always use karate . . . as soon as she learned how. Meanwhile, if the need were great, she could probably fake it.

Later that night Victoria walked back into her apartment, ready for the deep sleep boredom could so readily bring about. Date number one had been the epitome of what Victoria had expected: a total dud as far as she personally was concerned, but perfect for her interview. He was not quite five foot five, had acne carried over from his youth and he had admitted to being in his mid-forties. Forties? Hah! Even so, the evening went smoothly, as did the interview. If the others were as easy as that she'd have her article in no time, although she still hoped to uncover something out of the ordinary to make it special.

Her first date had been almost too pat, too much the stereotype of what she had expected to encounter. And that bothered her. Was she unconsciously choosing a particular type of man from the letters she received because she wanted to prove her own theory of what the typical man involved with a dating service was like? If that was the case, then she should pick someone totally different or her article wouldn't be completely fair or terribly interesting. The easy way out wasn't always the right way.

She nibbled on her finger as she glanced through the almost thirty other letters that had been sent to her by potential dates. Her second date was already chosen, but for her third date she would pick someone totally unlike the others. One letter, typewritten as if it were a piece of business correspondence, jumped out at her. This . . . she glanced down at the almost illegible signature, squinting to decipher the name Kurt Wentworth, was a businessman who loved to listen to women talk and was interested in a multitude of subjects; he especially liked opera and was a motor-cycle enthusiast.

She grinned. She didn't have a motorcycle, but her moped, a two-wheeled bike with a lawn-mower motor, was her main source of transportation. She appreciated it more with every rise in gas prices.

"Well, Mr. Wentworth," she murmured, "let's see what makes you tick!"

# 2

Victoria opened the door for her third date, one hand ready to slam it shut if the man standing in the hall wasn't wearing a brown shirt, the agreed upon identifying mark of her date. He was. It took a minute for her eyes to focus on anything other than the vee of very tanned chest that showed between the lapels of his shirt. She finally glanced up further to meet his eyes and was left almost breathless by his looks. His hair was a dark teak color streaked with golden blond, his eyes a rich chocolate brown that seemed reserved. He was a little haughty, slightly uncomfortable at being stared at and just as puzzled as she was. He had a classically square jaw that jutted with determination, cheeks that were slashed with lines that showed a definite sense of humor and a full, sensuous bottom lip that contrasted with his thinner top lip.

"Mr. Wentworth, I presume?" She smiled, knowing it probably looked more like a grimace, and hoped her voice didn't sound as disbelieving as she felt inside. What on earth was this man doing getting dates through a newspaper? Anyone as good-looking as he was could stand on any random corner of Los Angeles and pick up five women in just as many minutes! Her eyes widened with an alarming thought. Was he . . . abnormal or something? The *something* had her stumped.

"Am I allowed entrance?" His mouth quirked in response to her stare as he tilted his head to see the rest of her. Right now only a portion of her head was showing through the crack in the door.

The opening slowly widened and she reluctantly allowed him in, following him past her small kitchen and into the slightly larger living room. His gaze took in everything in a matter of seconds. Vicky was instantly reminded of a computer; he had assessed her furniture, the bright posters pinned to the wall, her slightly worn imitation oriental carpet and the desk and typewriter sitting in the nook that should have held a dining set. Then his eyes veered toward her, taking in the bulky navy-blue sailor suit, tightly pulled-back hair, too-large glasses that seemed to slip down her very petite nose every time she got agitated and the brown shoes that made her look as if she had just stepped off a mountain hiking path. Suddenly she wished she was wearing gold silk, high heels and a very sexy smile. At least she could have worn her contacts! Perhaps she had overdone the camouflage routine?

"The room is very attractive." His voice was low. Was he comparing her dull looks with the vibrancy of her decorating? Damn!

She took a deep breath and smiled sweetly, determined to make the best of this. She pushed away all thoughts of quickly changing into something he would notice with appreciation and walked with a determined step toward the small kitchen. "Thank you. Would you like a glass of wine before we leave?"

One dark brow rose and a smile continued to tug at the corners of his mouth. "Yes, please."

In the kitchen she deftly poured two glasses of a California chablis, taking a quick gulp before heading back into the room. She would need fortification if she were to get through this night with aplomb.

He sniffed the golden liquid suspiciously, then sipped cautiously, rolling the coolness on his tongue. "Very good," he pronounced.

"Did you expect something else?"

"I didn't know." His eyes raked her once more before he turned to stare at an art poster; then he glanced back at her again, obviously puzzled.

"It's good, but it's not an imported wine. I'm into keeping American money in America," she said almost defiantly, quickly forgetting that she had promised herself never to give personal opinions while doing research.

"Admirable, I'm sure."

"This is going to be quite a night," she muttered under her breath, for the first time wishing she had never started this.

"I beg your pardon?"

"I said, I love America with all my might." She smiled brightly at the wide-eyed stare he gave her. "Would you care for more?" Then she noticed that his glass was still half-full and a blush lit her cheeks. "No, I guess not," she mumbled. What was the matter with her? She had never met a man she couldn't deal with, so why was he getting to her like this? She was acting like a stagestruck schoolgirl! Though she promised to pull herself together, the next words just slipped out of her mouth.

"Are you trying to get into the movies?"

Once more he looked confused. Perhaps startled would have been a better word. It was obvious that he thought he had just walked into a mad hatter's party . . . after the tea had been served!

"No. Why?"

"I was just wondering. I mean, it's unusual to find such a good-looking man in tinsel town who isn't waiting for that 'big break.' "

She took another gulp of wine. At this rate she'd be saying goodbye just minutes after saying hello.

"No, I'm a businessman, like I said in my letter."

"What kind of business?" Please, let it be respectable!

"I . . . I'm in the paper industry." Now it was his turn to take a large gulp.

"How interesting!" She hoped her eyes had that "my, isn't that wonderful" look. If she could only make it through the next two hours she could call this interview quits. For some reason his dark brown eyes seemed to see right through her. It wouldn't be too long before he recognized her disguise for what it was and began to wonder why any woman would make herself so unattractive. "I'm into using things made from recycled paper, myself."

"I understand," Kurt said, apparently fed up with both the conversation and the wine. He placed the almost empty glass on the bar and turned to her expectantly. "Are you ready to go? I have reservations for seven."

"Right. Just let me freshen my makeup and grab my purse. Make yourself at home. I won't be a minute." Victoria almost ran down the small hallway to her bedroom and shut the door behind her, taking several deep breaths as she leaned heavily against it.

That man was potent! His entire body reeked of class, not to mention that latent sex appeal! Her mind whirled with possible reasons why he would need to find a date this way. He must have something wrong with him. But what? There was a definite mystery about him.

She glanced in the mirror, squinting through her glasses to see herself, then moaned aloud. He must really think she was nuts! There wasn't a spot of makeup on her face to replace or repair!

Mentally bracing herself, Victoria reached for her purse and the doorknob. She might as well face the man and get it over with. After all, she couldn't wait until he came into her bedroom looking for her to interview him. . . . For the first time in her twenty-four years she wondered why not.

". . . but Watergate *proved* that we have to keep politicians under constant surveillance!" She punched her point home in triumph, leaning back in her chair to sip the wine Kurt had ordered to accompany their Italian dinner. They had been arguing politics and current events all evening and it had been a stimulating discussion. They were both opinionated and knowledgeable—and on opposite sides of the fence. All in all it had been the best date of any sort Victoria had had in a long time.

Kurt thumped his hand on the table. "*Politician* is just a label we give to people. It's no different than saying *teacher* or *writer*. It's how each individual uses that title that makes the difference. You can't condemn all for one. It would be like saying that if one teacher secretly hates children, all teachers must secretly hate children. As my secretary would say, 'You're glumping.'" He grinned at her and suddenly the thread of the conversation was lost as she grinned back. Her face was flushed from the good food and wine, and the better conversation.

He glanced briefly at his watch before looking back at her ruefully. "Do you realize we've been talking almost four hours straight?"

"I had no idea." She grinned. "And I'm a working girl who has to be up at the crack of dawn."

They walked out a few minutes later, his hand disturbingly warm on her arm. "What do you do for a living? I forgot to ask."

"Wh-what?"

"I noticed that you had a typewriter in your apartment. Are you a secretary or a budding novelist?" he teased.

"Oh, both," she stated airily. "I'm a typist by day and a novelist by night." At least that wasn't too far from the truth.

"What's your novel about?" He opened the door of his slightly shopworn Ford and she slipped in, waiting until he reached his own side before answering.

"Romance. What else?"

"Isn't that a little trite? Especially in this day and age of promiscuity?"

She stiffened, on the defense. "And what's the last novel you've read?"

He named a best-selling spy novel.

"And isn't it a little silly to read about an ordinary man who does such extraordinary things with so little talent or knowledge? He outwits every master spy and he's never been in the business before! I'd say your style of book is far more unlikely than mine. At least romance happens every day in someone's life. How many spies do you know?"

His chuckle was deep, vibrating through the interior of the car. "I give up."

Victoria stared at his profile, loving the slash lines that grooved his cheeks when he smiled. He was a stimulating man, with more than his share of sex appeal. It just didn't fit.

He broke into her reverie. "Do you mind if I stop for a minute and get a pack of cigarettes?"

"It's your life." She shrugged, trying to act unconcerned. "But it seems a shame to cut it short with a habit that's both distasteful and dangerous."

He groaned. "Oh, no. Don't tell me you take vitamins, too."

Her eyes glittered with hidden laughter, but she answered in a totally sober voice. "Of course. One iron and two vitamin Cs a day."

His low laughter played along her spine. When his hand reached out and clasped hers she felt a sudden warmth flowing through her veins.

"Oh, Vicky! One thing I can say is that you'd never be boring! Opinionated, yes. Boring, no."

He pulled into a small all-night grocery store and opened the door. "And just to humor you, I'll buy a lighter brand than I usually do," he teased. "I'll taper off gradually."

She watched him walk with catlike grace toward the glass doors, her eyes following him inside, trying to imprint the image of him on her brain. This might be the last time she saw him, but she would never forget him.

She fiddled absently with the lock on the glove compartment, her mind elsewhere until the latch snapped open. Another puzzle. The compartment was immaculate except for a single folder. Without thinking she reached for it, her reporter's instinct ahead of her muddled thinking. The cardboard folder read STAR RENT-A-CAR in big bold letters. But before she could open it Kurt was walking out the glass doors and toward the car, so she quickly shoved it back where it belonged.

Why did he rent a car? Didn't he have one of his own? After all, the paper business couldn't be all that bad. In fact, the clothing he wore was expensive and the meal hadn't been cheap, either, even if he had chosen an out-of-the-way restaurant in a section of town she wasn't familiar with. Somehow she didn't think he had been there before, either. He had paid too much attention to the street names as they drove.

He gave her a slow, intimate smile before turning the key in the ignition. "Ready?"

For what? she wondered. "Yes."

The dim interior of the car gave the planes of his face a slightly sinister look and she involuntarily shivered.

"Cold?" Without asking he pulled her toward him, fitting her just under the curve of his shoulder and wrapping one arm around her to rest lightly on her waist.

"I bet you miss your motorcycle," she murmured, glancing out the window at the only starry night they had had in weeks.

"My what?" His look was incredulous. Victoria stared up at him, clearly puzzled.

"Your letter said you love motorcycles. I have a moped myself. I use it to save gas when I'm in town and don't have to travel the freeways."

"Is that very often?"

"What?"

"That you need to drive the freeways."

"No, thank goodness. Gas eats heavily into my budget as it is. I spend at least fifteen dollars a week on gas now."

"Is that all?" Once more he looked shocked.

"That's enough! I don't know how much you spend, but sixty dollars a month is enough of a financial dent for me!"

"How frugal." He smiled a small secret smile before openly grinning at what must have been a private joke. But his light squeeze at her waist took her mind completely off the fact that she had been asking about his own mode of transportation.

They were parked in front of her apartment house in less than fifteen minutes. Granted, those had been the longest minutes of silence since the evening had begun, but it had been companionable.

Suddenly she was stiff, not wanting the evening to end yet, but not knowing what he would think if she offered to extend it. "Would you like a cup of coffee?" Her voice sounded high-pitched and strained even to her own ears.

"I was hoping you'd ask."

When they reached the apartment door Kurt took the key from her hand and slipped it into the lock, then stood back to allow her entrance. A true gentleman.

Victoria quickly flipped on the overhead lights, then made a beeline toward the kitchen, plugging in the coffeemaker and going through the almost automatic motions of every morning's routine. When she was done she turned to find him leaning against the doorjamb, his arms crossed, his stance lazy. The living-room lights behind him were glowing a dim gold, letting her know he had rearranged the situation to fit his idea of a seduction scene. Somehow she knew he wasn't as relaxed as he looked.

"Come here," he said softly in a burlap-rough voice that played on her nerve endings.

She walked toward him slowly, hesitantly, knowing what was going to happen. But she suddenly wanted his touch almost as badly as his dark chocolate-brown eyes told her he wanted to hold her.

His arms enfolded her slim form, bringing his hard firm body in direct contact with hers. His legs were spread wide to block the doorway, forcing her to lean against him to keep her balance. One hand came up and gently slipped off her overlarge glasses.

"I think we can dispense with these now. You won't be needing them."

She lifted her eyes, standing passively in his arms, as he leisurely surveyed her face. Then his lips came down and slowly brushed hers, tentatively, hesitantly, until he felt her own natural response. His arms tightened perceptibly, one hand twining in her hair to hold her head while the other captured her waist to tease the small of her back and send warmth through her dazed limbs. A torrent of mixed emotions rushed through her body, sending scrambled responses back to her numbed brain. She had never been so affected by a man before. Never, and it frightened her beyond belief. Always in charge, Vicky had never believed in the possibility of being swept off her feet by a man . . . until now.

"You're so soft, so sweet-tasting." His voice was rough, sensuous, gliding against the nerves in her ears to heighten the taut pitch of her body. His tongue explored the warmth of her mouth and suddenly she was responding, no longer tense and alert, but fluid and feverish.

His hand slowly glided down to her shoulder, resting lightly and hesitating only a second before slipping further to capture a breast, teasing the nipple to taut attention as she arched invitingly toward his touch.

Her emotions swirled. Bells were ringing in her ears and flashes of brilliant light played in front her eyes.

She had always made fun of women who swore that fireworks really did happen, especially after reading descriptions in dozens of books. It had never seemed a possibility . . . until now. She relaxed against him, her body blending perfectly with his. His lips, tongue and hands were telling her he had the same reaction as they melded their bodies together in the doorway. Finally he broke the kiss and she leaned her head against his solid chest, feeling the warmth of his skin through his shirt and hearing his erratic heartbeat. Slowly their hearts resumed an almost normal rhythm.

He cupped her breast in his hand. "So nice, so sweet and sensitive," he growled in her ear. "I like that."

Victoria raised her head, continuing where he had left off. She nibbled on his full lower lip, spreading kisses along his strong jawline, burrowing her head into his neck. Her legs felt weak, her body strangely boneless. And certainly she had never felt so confidently aggressive in her whole life.

"Why?" she murmured between kisses.

His eyes were almost a dark golden hue as he stared down at her small heart-shaped face. Dimples bloomed in both her cheeks as she pursed her lips to give another feather-light kiss to the corner of his mouth. Her hair had come undone from its ponytail and her eyes glittered with passion.

"I don't know," was his only answer, surprising even himself. He had always gone out with more heavily endowed women, whether by chance or choice he wasn't certain. But he liked this woman just the way she was, slim, lithe, small-boned.

"Whatever the reason, I'm pleased that you're pleased, because there's not a thing I can do about it." She chuckled throatily.

The coffeepot finally finished perking and the silence covered them like a warm blanket. "I love your aftershave. I've never smelled that scent before." She twined her arms around his neck, playing with his hair, slipping a small nail around the curvature of his ear.

"It's a special brand." His finger outlined the curve of her lips and she opened them willingly for him to feel the moistness.

"I thought only women had scents made up for them."

His mouth hovered just above hers, teasing her with his nearness. "Men sometimes do it, too."

Her lips formed the word oh and it was just the perfect word for him to kiss.

The tip of his tongue traced the outline of her lips, exactly where his finger had been; then, with aching slowness, he pierced her mouth, seeking the deeper response she was totally willing to give. The erotic scent of his aftershave mixed with his definitely masculine smell. His slightly moist kiss, his gentle but firm touch, were the most erotic Victoria had ever felt.

His mouth moved downward, trailing over her chin to her slim neck and then to the small sharp vee of her dress, pulling it aside so he could reach the tender swell of her breasts. His hands were lightly touching all over her body, teasing here, taunting there, a ghost of glowing heat remaining where he had been, a fire stirring where his hands had moved. His soothing mouth and hands were persuading her to do things she had never thought to do before. Suddenly nothing seemed as important as this. All she wanted was him, and for this to go on forever.

Kurt took her hand, his eyes searching out the small darkened hallway to her room. "Let's go to your room and finish this," he murmured huskily, his other hand stroking her neck. "I'm too old to make love in kitchens. We can drink coffee later, when we're both ready for it."

The mist slowly dissolved for Victoria. She clearly saw the scene as someone else would see it. And it looked shabby. How could she explain that this wasn't her regular routine? That she usually didn't advertise in singles papers and then go to bed with every guy who answered her ad? She couldn't.

"I'm afraid not, Kurt."

He looked at her, eyebrows raised in derision. "Are we playing cat and mouse games? I thought you were an up-front person, one who expected others to say what they want, and not what's dictated by society."

"I *am* an up-front person, but that doesn't mean I slip in and out of bed with total strangers." Her brown eyes flashed in defense, ignoring the underlying sense of disappointment she felt. Why should she have thought he was any different from the rest of the men she knew? But she had.

"I wasn't accusing you of that, Vicky. I was accusing you of games." His hands stroked her arms lightly, his warm brown eyes playing across the features of her face before taking in the slim but well-shaped figure hidden beneath her dowdy clothing.

"I'm not playing games. That's just it." She stood firm.

"Your outlandish costume says you are." His arms dropped to his sides, a distant and cool look in his eyes. "I don't get it. You advertise in a singles newspaper that you're looking for the right guy, knowing you'd be asked to come across sometime."

"And also knowing I wouldn't." She took a deep breath, reaching for an explanation. "I just wanted to *meet* guys, I wasn't looking for a bed partner. I don't know you well enough to, to. . . ." Her voice faded off as she realized just how juvenile that sounded in a cosmopolitan city like Los Angeles where people met and went to bed in the space of an hour, let alone waiting five!

"You want me. You respond to me. We both know that."

"That doesn't mean I'll go to bed with you. It means that my body is willing, but my spirit won't let me."

He stiffened, his face rock-hard and implacable. "I see. You're a thrillseeker who advertises, but doesn't follow through." His eyes narrowed speculatively. "Or is it just *my* honor that you won't besmirch? Am I the odd man out because you respond too well to my touch and it frightens you?"

"Of course not!"

"Then why advertise?"

It was time to turn the tables. Two could get just as angry as one. "Why did *you* advertise? You could get a hundred dates with your looks, and yet here you are, dating me."

He looked away, his eyes gliding toward the bright cheery posters on the wall. "It was just an experiment."

"Experiment? Well, that's what it was for me, too." She turned away from him, walking toward the front door and holding it open to allow him to exit.

"Dammit! Shut that door and give me an explanation of what's going on!" He ran an agitated hand through his hair, staring at her in baffled anger.

"Please go. Now." Her hand shook as she turned the knob, but she wouldn't let him see how upset she was.

He strode toward the outer hall, hesitating only when he reached her side. "This serves me right," he muttered under his breath, barely loud enough for her to hear.

His steps echoed down the passageway and toward the elevator. Victoria listened quietly, afraid to move until she was sure he was gone. When the grinding of the old, rickety cables announced his departure she gave a sigh. So much for date number three, she told herself. And now it was time to wipe him out of her mind. She refused to accept the fact that he had made her feel like no other man ever had. This wasn't the time for introspection—this was research. Something told her to stay away from him; he was too volatile a mixture for her chemistry. She determinedly forced him out of her mind. Bending down, she slipped off her shoes. For looking so comfortable they sure caused blisters! Then she whistled her way to the bathroom. A warm bath with a good book and a glass of wine would do wonders for her nerves.

Why were all the good-looking, dynamic men either taken or taken up with their own prowess? She wouldn't admit, even to herself, that she had gone merrily along with his game plan without resistance right up to the last minute.

Victoria quickly shed the ugly blue dress and allowed her hair complete freedom while the bathwater ran. She glanced in the now steamy bathroom mirror, surveying her body as a man would see it. Her waist was slim, her hips only slightly fuller; her breasts were a nice average size, but certainly not voluptuous. Was she so ugly that he had decided she wasn't worth an all-out effort? Somehow that hurt more than any other thought.

# 3

Victoria woke up the following morning with a heavy pressure in her head. Had she slept a wink all night? She had faithfully promised herself that she wouldn't think another thought about Kurt Wentworth, yet there were so many pieces to the puzzle of the man that she couldn't put together.

His letter said he loved motorcycles, yet he had looked totally surprised when she had mentioned the subject. He had rented a car, but if it was to impress her, why rent a two-year-old Ford? He spent money for good food, but he went to a completely out-of-the-way restaurant. His clothing was expensive, but bought off the rack, while his aftershave was blended especially for him. He acted like the typical California swinging single, but his conversation was concise and to the point, with none of the slang Victoria was used to hearing. His thoughts were accurate; he was well-read and up to date on all the current news, domestic and foreign. But most of all, he was handsome as the devil, dripped with sex appeal, knew how to make love expertly and beautifully—but he advertised in a dating newspaper.

None of it made sense.

If he wasn't what he claimed to be, then what was he?

Her mind whirled with possibilities, discarding them all as she tried to dissect the man. Nothing gave her an answer that she could live with.

Finally she got dressed. Grabbing her notes on hotels that laid claim to having ghosts, she began the newest article assigned to her. If she did nothing else today she'd get through a first draft. Her checkbook told her she needed this money more than she needed to figure out Kurt Wentworth. After all, she had failed miserably as an interviewer last night, telling him more of her own opinions and asking fewer questions than she had ever done before in her life.

What had gotten into her that she had let the evening slip by without getting the facts she needed for her article? Irritation raised its ugly head, but she wasn't sure if she was exasperated with him—or with herself!

She resolutely aimed her thoughts and energy toward the typewriter so she could make sense of the notes at hand.

Kurt got to work early the next morning and for the first time in his life was in no hurry to tackle his enormous load of paperwork. As he strolled through the wide glass doors and into the lobby of the *Newstime* building, he unconsciously searched the crowd for a long-haired, big-eyed, slim but dowdily dressed young woman. He didn't even realize what he was doing until he found himself leaning against the far wall, watching the door expectantly.

He shook the placid expression from his face, more for his own benefit than anyone else's, and walked with a determined gait toward the closest elevator. Some of the women gave him a sultry eye, while others smiled invitingly. None of them seemed to have sense enough not to make themselves blatantly obvious.

He forced his mind to turn to today's business commitments. A guilty conscience made him promise to himself that he would give Julie a treat tonight, perhaps take her to that disco she'd been raving about. She was young and a starlet, and wanted to be seen by the right crowd. It wasn't Kurt's idea of a good time, but perhaps it would take his mind off . . . other things.

Much later that night he stared out at the bobbing boats in the harbor, their small twinkling lights forming a hazy pattern on the softly rolling waves. He glanced into his watery scotch and wondered why he even bothered to see Julie anymore, let alone pay the exorbitant bills she considered it necessary to incur. Her dress tonight, a deep green strapless jersey that clung like glue to show off her curves, was worthy of the body it encased, but the effect it had on him was nil. Her long red nails had clung tenaciously to his arm all night. Her hands could have been about his throat, he felt so suffocated by her nearness. He had finally loosened her grip and walked away to discuss the upcoming football season with a few of the other men before taking her home and leaving her there—alone.

What was wrong with him? He had everything a man could ask for: a corporation prestigious enough to be listed in *Dun & Bradstreet;* property; a charming, if clinging, mistress; time to do what he wanted. . . .

*To do what he wanted* was the key phrase. Without thinking he reached for the phone and dialed the number written on the pad.

"Hello, Victoria? This is Kurt."

Her voice was hazy with sleep. "Kurt who?"

"Kurt—uh, Wentworth. We went out to an Italian restaurant the other night." He sounded impatient.

"And you decided you wanted to call and reminisce at three in the morning?" She pushed back the hair that had fallen across her face, slowly sitting up and turning on the small bedside lamp to doublecheck the time. She was right.

"I decided to call and apologize." His voice held a tinge of humor. "And now I find out I must apologize again for the time. I'll call you again tomorrow. Goodnight."

"Wait a minute!" Vicky exclaimed, now sitting straight up and wide awake. "Now that I'm up you might as well continue."

His husky chuckle resounded in her ear and a small tremor feathered down her spine to thread through her veins and warm her insides. "I just wanted to say hello and that I'm sorry for my boorishness the night we went out. I'm afraid I assumed too much."

"Right," she stated. "And I accept your apology." She rested the phone on her shoulder and hugged her knees, suddenly feeling totally happy.

"Am I forgiven?"

"Of course."

"Enough for you to go out with me again?"

"Of course."

"If you had answered my question like that the other night I wouldn't have to be apologizing now," he teased.

"If I had answered your question like that you'd still be here," she retorted.

"Are you that sure of your staying power?"

"I'm that sure of *yours.*"

"So I did get through that Victorian shield of yours."

"Victorian!" she shrieked indignantly. "You're the one who's a mass of contradictions!"

Suddenly he sounded wary. "What do you mean?"

"I'll discuss it with you the next time we meet."

"Tomorrow at eight."

"I have a date then. The next night, same time."

He was surprised at his feeling of irritation. "Who with?" he snapped without bothering to hide his sudden feelings.

"No one you know. Is it a date or not?" She waited for his reply, trying to keep her heart from thumping into the phone.

"See you then. Oh, Victoria?" His voice softened.

"Yes?" She held her breath.

"Buy a new dress, one with a little style. The last one was definitely not you."

He hung up, smiling to himself. She had a lovely voice, even on the phone. His mind conjured up a picture of her as she had looked that night in his arms. Her eyes had been wide with discovery, her face flushed a becoming pink, her long hair loose and silky, flowing like dark soft rainwater through his fingers. . . .

He gulped down the remainder of his drink and walked briskly into the bedroom. Suddenly he was happy, but tired. What he needed was a good night's sleep.

Victoria was impatient for Kurt to come. She had dressed in a plain black cotton shirtwaist, her hair long and sleek down her back. She could see her reflection in the mirror and was pleased. She didn't want to ask herself too many probing questions concerning her feelings for Kurt Wentworth. Nothing mattered at this point but that he enjoy her company as much as she did his.

She jumped nervously when the doorbell rang, then walked sedately toward it, as if he could see her through the wooden door.

Her smile soon turned to surprise, however, when she found her uncle standing in the hallway with a sheepish smile.

"Hi, honey. Can I come in for a minute?" She grinned at his hesitancy, thinking that it looked like being there was the last thing he wanted to do. She tried to lighten his spirit by curtsying to allow him entrance.

"Of course. When my favorite uncle and landlord

calls he's always welcome," she teased, giving his arm a squeeze as he walked by. "What's the matter, Uncle Jake? You look lost."

He sat uncomfortably on the edge of the sofa, his glance taking in the small room. "Honey, I don't know how to tell you this, and I wouldn't bring it up unless I had no choice. You know that, don't you?" He begged her to understand and she automatically nodded, wondering what in heaven's name he was talking about.

"They say sharing a problem cuts it in half, so tell me what's the matter." She sat across from him, concern showing in her eyes.

"I, uh, I have to raise the monthly rent, honey. The roof needs fixing and so does the plumbing, and unless I can raise the rent I won't be able to cover the payments on the second mortgage I need." His eyes skipped around the room again before landing somewhere around her shoulder. "I waited as long as I could, but you know how it is. I'm in a bind, and you often said that the apartment was more than reasonable. And with today's prices . . ." His voice dwindled away uncertainly.

"Good grief," she muttered under her breath, suddenly seeing herself being unable to live within her budget, even if she could find a full-time job.

"It's either that or maybe you could find another place to live, one where the landlord doesn't have so many problems keeping up with inflation." He cleared his throat. "I'm sorry, honey."

She reached over and patted his hand absently. "I

know you are, and it can't be helped. You've been a rock these past years, Uncle Jake. It's my fault for not seeing it coming and preparing myself for it. I knew this rent was too good to last, but I just went blithely on my way." She turned over a multitude of alternatives in her mind, but she couldn't find a quick and sure answer.

"How much more rent money do you need?"

He named a figure and Victoria just closed her eyes. It wasn't an outrageous sum, but there was no way she could fit *that* into her existing budget, or find an extra job to cover it. She was sunk. There was no question that he could easily command that price for her apartment—correction, his apartment—but it still put her out into the street.

She decided to test the firmness of the ground gently. "You know you could probably ask my mother for the money and she'd get it for you."

He stiffened his already straight spine, his eyes snapping coldly. "No!" was his only answer.

She sighed, patting his hand to tell him that she understood. After all, she could probably ask her mother for her extra rent money and get it, but that wasn't her way. She hadn't tried to make it on her own over the past seven years, doing without if she had to, just to ask for money now. Uncle Jake and she thought alike. Never.

"When do you want me to move?" She looked up at her uncle and suddenly felt sorry for him. He didn't like this any better than she did. But that didn't help the immediate problem.

"I can give you the rest of this month, Vicky, but that's about it."

"Three weeks," she muttered under her breath, quickly figuring out her daily calendar and realizing that her budget might not even get her that far. "Don't worry. I'll think of something. It's not your problem, Uncle Jake."

His expression was so hangdog that she wanted to laugh, but she was afraid she just might loosen a tear and then he'd really be upset.

"If you can't find anything by then, perhaps you could move in with me. I've always got the couch," he offered, but she knew the old poker buddies who played at her uncle's a couple of times a week wouldn't take to that idea very well.

"I appreciate the offer, but I'm sure I can work something out. There's bound to be someone who needs a roommate to share a reasonable rent," she assured him with more bravado than she felt.

Five minutes after her Uncle Jake left the doorbell rang again. All the excitement she had felt earlier was now gone and she answered it absentmindedly, waving Kurt in as she tried to calm her churning thoughts with a glass of wine.

"Would you like a glass?"

"No, thanks. What's the matter?" he asked after a few minutes of almost total silence.

For the first time since he had arrived she looked, really looked, at him. He was wearing a pair of black slacks that had been molded to him and a brown silk shirt, open at the throat and rolled up at the cuffs. His hair was brushed into a studiedly casual style, his eyes crinkling into a slow smile. His hand cupped her chin as he silently stared down at the rounded outline of her mouth. Her heart reacted to his delving glance, jumping up into her throat as she watched him watching her. A primitive excitement coursed through her veins at the deliberately sensuous unspoken message she saw in his eyes and she silently answered affirmatively. Her hand led a teasing trail up his shoulder to circle his corded neck and slowly she brought his lips to hers in an almost innocent kiss as they greeted each other again. Victoria felt a shiver go down his spine, yet she knew that his reaction was no stronger than hers.

He reluctantly pulled away, his hands absently caressing her arms. His forehead rested on hers as they both caught up with their rocketing emotions.

"I still want you. Very much," he murmured huskily, his tone holding an element of surprise. "You know that."

Victoria nodded, unable to speak.

"Are you going to continue to say no?"

"I think we need to know each other better," she finally murmured.

"Why? You feel the same."

"Because I want to be loved by the whole man, not just the part that controls his passion."

He stiffened in her arms. "I'm not promising to love you, Vicky. I do promise that I want to make love to you. Those are two different things."

"Poor Kurt." Her voice was soft with muted laughter, slightly shaky. "Are you so afraid of the word love that you have to define everything you say, everything you feel?"

He relaxed. "I've been misunderstood before and I'd like to continue our relationship. I just want you to understand me."

"And I want you to understand me, too. That's exactly why we're waiting." She turned in his arms and forced herself to walk to the couch. She sat down and stared at him as he stood in the hallway. "So make up your mind. Do we go at my pace, or not at all?" She held up a hand as she talked. "I might as well warn you now. By the end of a few dates I might decide we're not suited and this goes no further." Her other hand was at her side and as she spoke she kept her fingers crossed as she mentally repeated a silent prayer. She had never been so affected by a man before and to call it off now would be like putting a lid on breathing.

His eyes twinkled ruefully. Even to Victoria it was obvious that he wasn't used to having someone else call the shots. "All right. We'll get to know each other and then see where it leads."

She stood and flipped back her hair, oblivious to the dramatic change in her appearance since the last time he had seen her, and when she looked up and saw the look of appreciation in his eyes she smiled in return.

"Ready to go?"

He seemed to be in another world and her words brought him back to earth. "What?"

"I said, are you ready to go?" She pronounced the

words slowly, dimples appearing like magic at the corners of her mouth.

"Yes. Where should we go? And where are your glasses? They were so thick they couldn't have been part of that costume you were wearing."

"Last date you chose the place, so now it's my turn. And my glasses are in my bedroom. I usually wear contacts." She had reached for her purse, then put out her hand for him to clasp as they walked to the door of the apartment. He hesitated just a moment before accepting her hand, perhaps still wary of showing more commitment than he felt. "And that 'costume' was just an old dress that did its job quite adequately."

"Except with me."

"Except with you," she agreed softly. "But then, there's an exception to every rule."

"There certainly is," he muttered under his breath, giving her hand a light but possessive squeeze that warmed her whole body. His eyes spoke volumes, blatantly expressing what his words hadn't said.

A little over an hour later he was muttering disbelievingly under his breath. She had dragged him into a pizza parlor whose specialty was the "everything" pizza, then eaten six pieces by herself. It was hard to believe that such a slender woman could eat so much. Most women he knew didn't eat more than a salad.

They both had a beer while Kurt looked around the 1920s-style parlor.

Her eyes gave him a teasing look. "Cheer up. The way you're carrying on someone would think you've never been to a pizza parlor before."

"One would, wouldn't one," he grumbled, glancing over his shoulder at a group of teenage boys standing around an electronic video game, their whoops of joy or moans of despair occasionally splitting the air.

She stopped chewing. "You really haven't, have you?" Her tone was incredulous, but his expression confirmed her suspicions. "Where in the world have you been living? On the moon?"

"Surprisingly enough, right here in L.A. until four years ago when I moved to Santa Barbara." He glanced around. "But you're wrong. I used to live in places like these when I was in college." He stared back at her. "I see life continues. . . ." He muttered the last sentence under his breath as one of the boys gave a victory cheer that rent the air.

She shook her head, her dark mahogany hair swinging back and forth in a shiny cascade. "Oh, no. You don't get to look down your aristocratic nose at us plebeians, mister. Now that I've satisfied my hunger I'm going to teach you how to play Destroyer. And you're going to like it." She stood and held out her hand. "Consider it a growth experience."

She sat him down at a small electronic table, then took the seat opposite him, putting her hand out for the quarters she had told him to get earlier. He handed them over, an indulgent grin on his face as he watched her slip them in the slot and turn the machine on.

"Now watch me," she said, and began firing away, shooting the enemy that darted between her blockades as the enemy shot back and the score added up.

Victoria leaned back, a smile on her face. "There, see how it's done? Your turn."

Kurt's smile was still indulgent, humoring her. The game flashed on and he began hitting the buttons, his smile turning to a frown of concentration.

When it was over Victoria gave him a look of appreciation. "That was great! I've never seen anyone get nine hundred points on their first try!"

"Put another quarter in there, will you, Victoria?" he mumbled, studying the game plan and points chart, totally occupied with a new toy.

"Again?"

"Mmmmm." His next score was even more impressive, as were his next and his next. By his fifth game his face was flushed with victory. He gave her a huge smile, sat back and sipped on the now warm beer. From the look on his face she could see that he was definitely proud of his accomplishment.

"Congratulations." She smiled sweetly.

"Thank you. It wasn't bad, was it?"

"I meant on your singlemindedness. Your games speak for themselves."

One brow rose, a smile still tugging at his sensuous lips. "Jealous of a machine, Victoria?" he murmured seductively, now concentrating totally on her. "You won't let me do anything else. I have to find my enjoyment where I can." He hesitated. "That is, unless . . . ?" He raised one dark brow in question, letting the unfinished sentence dangle, and she felt her skin warm under his look.

Victoria shifted, only to touch his knee with hers,

and she jerked back, ignoring his knowing look. "We can leave now . . . if you want to do things at my pace." His husky voice was low so the surrounding people couldn't hear, but firm enough that it brought every nerve in her body to life.

"This pace is good enough for me," she said primly, knowing that what she wanted most was to be held in his arms, his full lips pressing against hers. He seemed to be able to reach inside her easily, frighteningly and, most of all, excitingly. Fear and fascination blended together to put a sparkle in her eyes.

"That's what I thought, Victoria. So I won't push— right now." His look seared her skin. "But don't expect me to be good forever. Sooner or later we'll have a meeting of our bodies. It's what we both want."

She ignored his remark. She couldn't deny it.

The rest of the evening passed quickly. They played a few of the other machines, Victoria winning most games by a very small margin. But several times she lost badly, unable to concentrate with Kurt standing so near to her. His arm would brush hers, his thigh touch hers, and her heartbeat became erratic.

A few hours later, their quarters spent and both satisfied that they had played well, Victoria waved goodbye to the bartender and led Kurt outside into the cool night air.

She took a deep breath. "Lovely, isn't it? Especially at night, when the smog isn't so obvious. Sometimes I swear I can smell the sea."

"You aren't that far away from it." His voice held a tinge of humor.

"Oh, I know. It's just that Los Angeles doesn't conjure up visions of high surf and rolling waves, but"—she shrugged philosophically—"it's the best we can do when we have to earn our daily bread." As the mental image of her almost bare cupboard came to mind she thought that she wasn't even doing that right.

They strolled down the street, Kurt unaware of where she was leading, but not caring much, either.

"Here we are." She pushed open the glass-fronted door of Hal's Hot Dog Stand, allowing the mixed aromas of onions, relish, mustard and sizzling hot dogs to waft in his direction, helping it with her waving hand. "Isn't that great? Hal makes the best hot dogs in town."

He groaned. "A hot dog! Just what I need after shoveling down a pizza that held everything edible and a few things that probably weren't!"

"You didn't eat it alone," she said matter-of-factly. "I helped, too, to the tune of six pieces."

"And you're still hungry?"

"Pitting my expertise against yours on those machines made my appetite raise its ugly head. Besides, I'm not as rich as you are. For all you know this could be my first meal since our last date."

His eyes narrowed as they took a seat in the far corner of the room. "How do you know I'm rich?"

The tired waitress came over and Victoria ordered for both of them. Two orange drinks and two foot-long hot dogs, with everything. Once the waitress had retreated Vicky picked up on the conversation as if they had never been interrupted. She was surprised

57

that Kurt had stiffened so noticeably as he waited for her answer. Wasn't it obvious?

"Because you wear clothing that yells 'expensive,' you've driven two different cars on two different dates, and you have more credit cards than I can count," she said calmly, looking him straight in the eye. His eyes skittered away, but not before she saw relief registered there.

"So I gave myself away." His smile was warm.

It was time for a change of tactics. "Why are you involved with a dating magazine when you could get women on your own?"

The waitress interrupted them once again, giving him a moment to gather his thoughts. The drinks and hot dogs were set before them and Victoria plunged into hers immediately.

"Truth, now," she warned before taking a bite.

"I'm not 'involved.' I just answered your ad." His eyes were blank, giving nothing away.

"Why?" This obviously needed a very direct approach.

"I wanted to see what would happen. Curiosity, I suppose." He shrugged, then sipped his orange drink. It wasn't bad.

"You don't strike me as the sort of person who does things on the spur of the moment. I'd say everything you did was rather well-thought-out, deliberate, planned ahead."

"And you know me that well?" One brow rose in derision.

"I don't think anyone knows you well," she answered with a lot more insight than he wished she had.

"And what about you? Why did you put an ad in that paper?" He turned the tables, but she was ready for him.

"Unlike you, I *am* the type to do something that quixotic. I thought it might be fun to see what would turn up. Who knows, there may be a story in it." Her eyes were innocent, but he could see a touch of merriment twinkling there. It intrigued him.

"What kind of story? For a newspaper? Magazine? What?"

"For a new romance, of course." Her lips curved in a provocative smile.

"Oh, yes. The romance," he murmured before taking a bite of his second dinner, a small smile plastered on his face. If Margie could see him now she'd never believe it! He hadn't ventured into pizza parlors or hot dog stands since his college days, let alone spent an evening playing video games . . . and enjoying it!

"What's so funny?" Her eyes narrowed suspiciously. Was he laughing at her?

"I was just thinking of a friend of the family. If she saw me now she'd think I was losing my mind." He took another bite and washed it down with his drink. He hesitated before looking at her, his gaze warm and very sincere. "And I'm enjoying myself thoroughly."

Her smile took his breath away. The muscles of his chest tightened and he clenched his free hand to keep himself from reaching out and pulling her to him so he could kiss her into keeping that look. Slowly her smile softened and dimpled her cheeks, her eyes locked to his as they both felt the immensely powerful draw of physical attraction.

The waitress came to check on things and the spell was broken. They began to talk of mundane subjects.

He had a mother and three sisters living in San Francisco. He enjoyed seeing them, but business kept him occupied most of the time. He owned various properties around the city, but he didn't say where or how many.

She had a mother and a brother. They lived in another state and she didn't see them very often. He sensed rather than heard her hostility, but had sense enough not to pry. He learned that her uncle owned the small apartment building where she lived and the reason for her occupied mind when he had picked her up this evening. A new place was hard to find, especially at a low rent.

"And your father?" he asked softly.

"I have none," she answered simply, her face freezing into a mask. He didn't push.

After they got into the car, while he was driving her home, Kurt's arm went around her, pulling her slim form next to his as if it were the most natural thing in the world. She gave a light sigh, fitting herself against the curve of his body, one hand resting on his shoulder, the other on his muscled thigh. The music on the radio was low and soothing, wrapping them in a private cocoon amidst the lights of Los Angeles. His breath fanned the top of her head, his arm tightening possessively as they turned onto her street.

"Victoria." His voice was just a whisper in the confines of the car. He had parked in front of the dimly lit apartment, but neither had made a move to get out. "I have an apartment you can use." He was as surprised as she was by his offer. He had never intended to say that; it had just popped out.

Her body went taut, her hand pushing against the broad breadth of his chest. "No," she said emphatically, much to his surprise.

Moments before he had been berating himself for offering it, now he was intent on having her accept. "Why not? It's vacant and you need somewhere to live."

She stared up at him, searching his face to find the truth. "Why isn't it rented?" He could feel her withdrawing from him and silently cursed himself for his bad timing.

"It's just been vacated and I haven't had a chance to place an ad yet. I'd like you to take it."

She relaxed slightly, but not enough to fit back into the comfort of his embrace, where he wanted her. Why was she so skittish? Did she think strings were attached? He found he liked the idea, but kept that fact to himself. She was fun to be with, exciting, asking for nothing—which was a novelty. But she was still just another woman. Right? Right! He almost convinced himself.

"No strings attached?" she asked him, still cautious, still disbelieving.

"Only the ones you care to attach," he said solemnly.

She immediately became more practical. "Where is it and how much is the rent?"

He pulled her back into the curve of his arm, resting his cheek on the top of her head, his hand straying to rest lightly just below her breast. "It's a townhouse where the old Warner lot used to be. What are you paying now?"

She gave him the figure and he made a noise deep in his throat. "I'll give it to you at the same price. It's reasonable." He turned her chin up so he could see her reaction, but his eyes were sidetracked, staring at her firm, round, perfectly shaped mouth. Without another thought his lips closed over hers, sweetly, tenderly molding hers to fit the curvature of his as he slowly drew a response from her.

His soothing hands and questing tongue were all that Victoria felt and she gave in to his lead, her head drifting back to rest on his arm, her small breasts thrust forward to touch the silky fabric of his shirt as he shifted to lean above her. Her arms wound around his neck, one hand cupping the back of his head while her other hand strayed to his neck, running a tingling fingertip down the tautened muscles. Her mouth opened willingly, holding nothing back from his exploration. His hand left her ribcage to stroke her back and bring her closer to him. She obliged, melding to him with a childish eagerness to please and be pleased.

If she had any thoughts at all they were chaotic. It was wonderfully exquisite to be in his arms. It was also something she had never experienced before in her life and it overwhelmed everything else.

A low moan came from somewhere deep in his

chest and his hand strayed down to the hem of her skirt, pulling it up with an urgency that scared her.

"No." Her voice was soft, but her small hand on top of his relayed the message instantly.

"You're right. We should go inside and be comfortable. I haven't necked in a car since I was sixteen." His voice rasped against her nerves like sandpaper against silk.

"I mean no, period."

His eyes widened as her point got across. He smiled ruefully. "I see. Still at your pace." She confirmed it with a nod. "I'm a grown man, Vicky. I don't like waiting like this. Games aren't fun anymore."

"I'm not playing a game. And if you think I am, then perhaps we'd better not see each other." She moved out of his arms and slid across the seat to the door. "Thank you for allowing me to show you my idea of a good time. I enjoyed it."

The door was open and she was gone before he even had time to answer. He slammed his hand against the steering wheel, cursing under his breath, but he didn't drive away until he saw the light go on in her apartment.

Victoria watched the car drive away, tears stinging her eyes. Somehow Kurt Wentworth had gotten closer to her than she had ever allowed anyone else to get. Why did he have to be just another man on the prowl, looking for a night of sex the way other men hunted for trophies to hang on a den wall? Did it give them a vicarious thrill to discuss their prowess over and over, impressing others with their virile masculinity? Her own opinion of men had always been low; they were constantly looking for bodies instead of minds, but this was the first time it had mattered so much.

Damn herself for being such a fool!

# 4

Victoria? How are you, dear? I didn't receive a letter from you last month and I was worried." Her mother's voice sounded faint and tired.

"I'm fine, Mother. How are you feeling?" Worry overcame the usual emotional distance she kept from her mother. Although she didn't live with her or visit often, she still loved her, even if she couldn't always respect her.

"I'm doing well. The chemotherapy treatments are working, even if I do feel as limp as a dishrag for a day or two afterward." Her mother's soft sigh came over the wires, tightening like a cord around Victoria's chest. "Your father spends as much time as he can with me, and that makes it easier."

Victoria's heart hardened. "How nice. And how does he manage to do that without letting his wife, his children and his voters know?" Her voice was laced with sarcasm.

"Can't you ever forgive, Victoria?"

"No, I can't. The fact that he's been remarried for twenty years and still tries to pretend to us that we're his family is repugnant to me. We're swept aside so his career won't be publicly tinged with the dirt of another family, legal or not, sitting in the corner of the state to wait at his beck and call." Victoria heaved a breath, sorry she had ever said anything. It was old ground and neither her mother nor she was going to change her opinion at this late date. It had all been rehashed too often in the past; the present was constantly filled with the remembrance of it.

"I'm sorry, Mother. Tell me, how is Brent? Is he doing all right?"

Relief tinged her mother's voice. "He's doing very well. He'll graduate next month, as you know. I think he's going to make a fine lawyer. Your father is so proud of him."

But not proud enough to attend the graduation, I bet, Victoria thought to herself. "I'm glad," she said aloud.

"What have you been doing lately? I haven't talked to you in so long. Is everything all right? Do you need anything?" Her mother's querulous voice persisted.

Suddenly Victoria was tired, mentally and physically. "I'm fine, Mother," she lied. "I'm looking for a new apartment, something a little larger. My book is in the first-draft stage and I'm still working as a freelance writer. Everything's fine."

The conversation continued desultorily, Victoria feeling guiltier by the minute as she realized that her mother's health really was going downhill. If only she had the courage to go home. But seven years ago her world had come to a standstill and she had left, vowing never to return as long as her father, the great Senator Branden of Nevada, was around.

Finally the conversation came to an end and Vicky vowed never to get behind in her letter writing again. As long as she wrote regularly her mother wouldn't call. And as long as her mother didn't call Victoria wouldn't remember that terrible night when she had left or dwell on the painful years that had led up to it.

Her mother was a sweet, charming, typical southern gentlewoman whose one love in life was a man she had divorced over twenty years ago. They had met when she was just a child of sixteen, then met again when she was twenty-one, and she had once more fallen in love with the tall, somewhat overbearing man. Stephen Branden, ten years older, had been seeking a wife who would enhance and embrace his career in politics. He married his southern belle, but they both quickly realized just how ill-prepared she was to wear the heavy cloak of duty and withstand the constant political and public pressures that someone in his position had to become accustomed to. Within four years her mother had divorced Stephen, taken back her maiden name of Brown and bought a small house in the corner of the state, where she raised her family in peace and solitude. But Stephen still needed a wife who would be an asset, and found another, remarrying just one year later to a woman whose social graces were well-known throughout the entire state. They were still married and even had a daughter from that marriage.

It wasn't until Victoria was fourteen that she realized

what type of man her father was. She had grown into her early teens, never looking beyond the small sheltered world of her neighborhood. She knew her parents were divorced and she and her younger brother accepted it. That was the way it had been since before she could remember and no matter how much they wished it was different, nothing they knew of would bring their mother and father back together. And when Daddy came to visit they were happy together, a real family for a while. So when the shock of reality came it left her reeling for weeks.

One day, when she was seventeen, her dad had come to visit with a friend. They had gone downtown to do some shopping. While they walked down the street, her father telling her a few anecdotes concerning the last bills that had been passed, someone shouted to them. When they turned around Victoria could feel her father's arm stiffen and saw his face turn white. A young girl, perhaps four years younger than Victoria and prettier than anyone she had ever seen, stood in front of them. She reached up and gave Stephen Branden a kiss on the cheek.

"Daddy, what are you doing in Reno? I thought you didn't approve of gambling," she teased.

Interested spectators stopped to watch the group of youngsters across the street, creating a small crowd on the sidewalk. And, somehow, Victoria knew that her father was becoming more angry and frustrated at every person who stopped.

When it was over Victoria stood rooted to the sidewalk, her mouth moving, but no words formed. Her father's friend took her arm in his and patted her on the shoulder. Victoria barely remembered what had happened. She had been introduced as a daughter of a friend, and then her father had made excuses as to why he was there, his darting glances looking for reporters as he told the beautiful tall girl to be good and go back to her classmates, who were in town for a school-sponsored tour.

Somehow they made it home and Victoria found her way to her bedroom. Her father had gone directly to her mother's room. She had heard the door shut quietly and the low hum of voices. Everything else was blocked out.

For the first time her parents' way of life became a blinding reality, and the reality wasn't at all romantic or nice: It was shoddy and shabby, bringing home the fact that she—not the other girl—was the one who meant nothing to him. She was the one with no claim, no rights to her father's life—and nothing could change that except her father. And he wouldn't. It had all been spelled out to her in the five-minute episode on the sidewalks of Reno.

Finally she slept, but when she awoke her father, tired and worried, sat by her bedside, holding her hand as if it were a lifeline.

"I'm sorry, princess," he murmured.

"Why didn't you introduce me, Dad?" Her voice rasped in her throat from all the crying she had done.

"It would only have embarrassed you both." His head hung down on his chest.

"Or the one who's useful. Our family never seemed as sordid as it did at that moment. You come here and act as if we're all a family again. We all pretend; even

Mama dresses up and has your favorite meals ready. She plays your favorite records—almost as if you were dating. And you let us pretend!"

"I deserve that, princess, I know. But there's so much you don't understand."

Her voice sounded old and tired. "Now I do. All these years, since the beginning of high school, I've known about you and Mom, but I thought it was romantic, thwarted love, and all that. But today I saw it for what it really is." Her voice hardened. "You have a perfect family you can show off to the public and the press, and when you get tired of your public image you can come here and . . . and slum!" Her voice cracked, but her resolve was strong. "And I'll never forgive you. Never." She stared straight into his eyes. "I'll hate you for the rest of my life."

"Darling, don't say that. You're my daughter, my own flesh and blood." His eyes begged for understanding.

"Would you like to repeat that scene today and tell that girl, your other daughter, that? Would you tell the world? Of course not; I'm just an embarrassment. I'm not picture-perfect, a help to your career. You deny me, so I don't see why I can't deny you, too."

"I've tried to protect you and your mother," he protested. "I didn't want you to live in the spotlight, where there's no peace. You wouldn't have liked it, princess."

"It's all right for one child to live in the spotlight, but the other one can't handle it, is that what you're saying? Or is the fact that Mother hates crowds and I look like a tomboy a factor in your decision?"

70

He didn't answer, and it underlined Victoria's first impression that, whatever happened, if Stephen Branden had anything to do with something, he would be watching out for his own interests all the time.

"By keeping us in a closet you've been cheating both families. We're all fair game now. Thanks, *Senator Branden.* For nothing."

She stood then and reached for her overnight case, grabbing things and shoving them in helter-skelter.

"What are you doing?"

"I'm leaving. I'll never return as long as you're free to come here." She turned slowly and looked him up and down. "I hate you," she stated calmly. "I hate you more than I hate anyone. I never want to see you or *either* of your families again."

His voice had grated with anger and determination. He was every inch the senator. "You're not going anywhere, young lady. You're staying here. I'm locking you in until your mother comes and talks to you. Maybe she can explain better than I can." He hesitated at the door. "I do love you, princess. Remember that."

His look softened; he was silently pleading with her to give a little. He turned and left, locking the door behind him.

Victoria finished packing, picked up her purse and walked to the window. The ground was no more than six feet below the windowsill and she dropped her case out the window, then jumped down. She headed directly for her car, a shiny red Mustang she had received for her sixteenth birthday. Her father had always been generous with his money, even if not his time. Within seconds she was gone, heading across the desert to Los Angeles.

Six weeks later her father had traced her and found her waitressing in a small restaurant off the Strip. He had begged, pleaded and cajoled, but to no avail. He refused to give her the one thing she demanded, the only thing that mattered: public acknowledgment of her place in his life.

She stirred herself from the couch. It did no good to think of things past. All she got for her trouble was a bad case of melancholy.

Forcing herself to forget the phone call, she went back to the typewriter. Her book was coming along nicely, better than she had expected. All she had to do was remember what it was like to be in Kurt's arms and the words began to flow. Unfortunately, that also sharpened her awareness of him, and of his absence.

She continued to mull over his offer of a townhouse. Would that put her in the same position as her mother? She wanted no part of that! On the other hand, was she turning down a good thing because of misplaced pride? She didn't know.

The phone rang once more that day, but it was only someone trying to sell real estate in the canyons north of the city. She politely said no, then sat and hoped it would ring again.

She didn't want to admit to the disappointment she felt when Kurt didn't call, but her honesty wouldn't allow her to overlook it. He was becoming a part of her life, and it both frightened and excited her.

She called it quits late that afternoon, showering and then slipping into a short, front-buttoning terry robe before she went into the kitchen to nibble at a salad and sip a glass of chilled chablis. She opened a book and began to read, forcing herself to become immersed in the lives of the characters rather than staring out the window like a lovesick calf. Finally she began to relax, unwinding after her mother's phone call.

A knock announced a visitor. Victoria glanced at her watch and realized it was time for Gina to get home from work. She lived only two blocks away and usually dropped in two or three times a week for a quick chat before heading for her own apartment.

Without giving it another thought, Victoria opened the door, a ready smile in place. "You're just in time for a sala—"

She quickly backed away from the door, staring into Kurt's stony face.

"Hasn't anyone ever told you not to open the door to strangers? Don't you realize you could be raped or killed for pulling a stupid stunt like that?" he growled, pushing the door until it was opened far enough for him to slip through, then closing it behind him. Kurt stood in her small hallway, dwarfing both her and the apartment. His deep brown eyes registered her brief clothing and the smooth silkiness of the skin that was exposed. They grew darker with emotion before flitting back to her face, warming even more as his hunger for her grew.

He reached out and pulled her close to him, a deep sigh echoing in his throat as he nuzzled her neck, filling his nostrils with the clean, sweet scent of her. Not a word was spoken as his lips finally claimed hers, teasing her slightly pouting mouth into moving perfectly against his. He gave a deep, contented sigh, suddenly realizing that he had been waiting for this moment all day long. Being in her arms was like coming home.

It seemed perfect to Victoria, too, and when he kissed her she instantly decided to lead him where her heart told her she really wanted to go.

It wasn't that she had ever been afraid of giving herself to a man, but that she had always waited for the right man to come along. As frightening as the realization was, she was sure that Kurt was that man. Guided by instinct alone, she took his hand and led him into her bedroom. Her fingers gave his a light squeeze, silently telling him that this was what she, too, wanted.

Her smile reminded him of the Mona Lisa: small, secret and very, very beautiful. A lump formed in his throat at the thought of having her wrapped in his arms, holding her close. Everything else fled his usually orderly mind, including the reason why he had come to see her in the first place.

She pulled off his suit jacket, folding it neatly over a small chintz-covered chair in the corner of the golden room. Then she turned and loosened his tie, slipping it off his neck and tossing it to rest on top of his jacket. His shirt followed. Her hands trembled at the next step, but when she reached lower his hand stilled hers, his eyes blazing down to sear through to her soul.

"Are you sure?"

"Yes," she said simply. Her hand cupped his chin, feeling the quickened pulse beneath his jawline, and she knew that she affected something in him just as much as he affected her.

Still he wouldn't let it go. "Why now? Why not last night, or the night before?"

Her eyes gazed honestly into his. "Because I wasn't ready last night or the night before. I'm ready now." She didn't add that she knew in her heart that she had already committed herself to him. "Are you?"

He grinned as the realization of her capitulation hit home. "Yes," he murmured hoarsely, enfolding her tightly in his arms. His possessive embrace clearly showed the overwhelming need he felt for her and a small answering tremor passed through her body.

His kiss was rough but restrained, his hands wandering to the buttons of her short robe, allowing the fabric to fall at their feet. In moments he, too, stood naked, poised on the threshold of ecstasy.

She looked up, only to be torn apart by the hungry, open look on Kurt's face. They stared at each other for a long time. He was the master, standing so tall and straight and beautiful that it made her heart ache. And she, she was . . . her mind didn't have time to complete the thought. He bent, his large hands firmly circling her upper arms as he gently pulled her into his embrace, kissing her smile away and replacing it with a longing that grew deep inside like a slowly blown-up balloon. One arm moved to rest behind her knees as he picked her up and carried her to the bed, placing her carefully in the center before joining her, skin exquisitely touching skin along the entire length of their bodies.

His mouth touched her eyelids, the gentle curve of

her cheeks, then the hollow places of her arched throat, seeking the response he wanted and she gave so openly.

An almost unbearable tension quickened in the pit of her stomach as he continued his teasing. Suddenly she could stand no more and her hands pressed against his chest to push him back against the pillows. His eyes flew open in surprise and she smiled in reassurance as she began taunting his hair-roughened chest as he had taunted her. She explored him, her small nails caressing here, biting sweetly into his flesh there. She bent her head, flicking his hardened nipples with her tongue, only to hear a gasp torn from his throat, to feel his stomach tauten sharply in reaction. She caressed his inner thigh, her eyes locked with his. Her fingers teased his flesh from hip to knee, watching him, studying him, loving him.

Neither wanted to miss the expressions flitting across the other's face. The hunger was there, always, but so were surprise, sweet tenderness and an overwhelming warmth as they edged toward completion and fulfillment.

She smiled slowly, secretly, as she straddled his lean hips. Her long dark hair cascaded over one shoulder to brush against his chest, teasing his flesh as if it was another hand with which to taunt him. She bent down, her lips lightly stroking his without resting to complete the kiss. She tantalized him with her nearness, yet gave him only a taste of what he wanted. He reached up, holding her head still so he could capture the nectar of her mouth, taking what she had promised with her eyes.

His hands cradled her hips, pushing, pulling, lifting, as he wordlessly told her what to do. But still he didn't complete their union, allowing her to keep the lead until he could stand no more.

Suddenly he had reached his limit, and so had she. His arms encircled her and he rolled her down beneath him, his heavy body stretched over hers, the bulk of his weight resting on his strong arms as he suckled one small firm breast until she moaned her plea.

"Now, now," she begged breathlessly.

"Say please," he demanded.

"No!"

"Then I will. Please, Victoria?" His head bent, once more tasting her lips.

Then there was no more teasing, no more taunting of each other as the overwhelming passion that devoured both of them was brought to its fulfillment.

He entered quickly, easily, then was startled, but not enough to stop. He soothed her with sounds that formed no words, but their meaning was clear. She answered with kittenish noises from deep in her throat that could only be halted by his deepening kiss. His tongue battled with hers and she allowed him supremacy in the end.

She clung to his broad shoulders, feeling herself being carried to the heavens and placed on soft fluffy clouds of complete and total contentment.

She lay quietly in the curve of his strong arms as they caught their breath, hearts slowing down gradually to beat in unison. His hand brushed away the small wisps of hair at her temple; his other hand stroked her side before coming to rest, possessively cradling her breast.

She glanced up at him through her lashes, trying to gauge the depths of the man she had just given all of herself to. Did he know of her gift? Did he realize how much it meant, or was she just another woman in another bed in his life? She was afraid to know the answers, but not knowing was even worse.

He was looking down at her with half-closed eyes, a small, triumphant smile tugging at his firm lips. He shifted slightly, holding her in a tighter grip.

"Why, Victoria?"

She ran her hand across his chest. "Stop being so analytical. What is, is. That's all. It was *right.*"

"You're moving into the townhouse tomorrow. I'll take care of you from now on," he said with satisfied conviction.

"No," she answered softly, but with equal firmness.

"Okay, then you'll pay me the agreed-upon rent."

"No."

"And have the place completely to yourself," he continued as if she hadn't spoken. "Except when I'm invited over for dinner or come by to take you out. Or in case something else crops up and you decide you want company for the night," he teased, but there was a thread of strength in his words.

"No."

"And we'll take it easy, each learning the other gradually. We'll build our relationship stone by stone until it has a strong, firm foundation."

"No!"

He quirked one dark eyebrow. "You don't want a strong foundation?"

"I don't want to move into your townhouse," she said with exasperation lacing her tone. Was he obtuse or just playing at it? Didn't he see that she wanted him to recognize her as a giver, not a taker? Didn't he see that she needed his approval, not his bed? Did she have to spell it out?

"I don't want to continue our relationship this way. This was just a onetime thing, Kurt." She tried to explain, but it came out all wrong.

"You mean you want this to be a one-night-stand?" His expression was one of mock astonishment.

"No, I mean that I gave myself to you because I wanted to, not because I wanted to pay you for anything."

He turned serious at once. "I never thought of any other reason, darling. That's why I don't want to let you go. Not until we've had a chance to explore each other as people. Why not do that where I can keep an eye on you? You're much too trusting and vulnerable."

"I've taken care of myself since I was seventeen, Kurt. I think I can manage on my own," she said dryly. "Besides, you have your business to think of. Things to do and places to go, to quote a phrase. And so do I. I take care of myself; no one takes care of me." The last sentence was stated with so much conviction Kurt couldn't think of an answer.

Somewhere along the line, he realized, she had decided that being a mistress was not for her. Instead of irritating him, it somehow made him feel more protective toward her. She was totally different from most of the women he knew. But could that difference be the one defense that he would be unable to breech? His usually clearcut thoughts were becoming clouded with emotion and it bothered him. He had never been uncertain before where women were concerned. . . .

He gave a silent grimace. They'd discuss it tomorrow. He would explain it to her until she agreed with him. But right now he needed to make her trust him, so he gave her a long kiss and then changed the subject. Better to lose this battle than lose the whole war. . . .

Victoria pushed back a strand of hair from her neck. The day was hot and muggy; Los Angeles was wrapped in smog and the fumes burned her nostrils and throat. She spent the morning looking at apartments, most of which weren't worth a tenth of what she had been paying. The few she liked had rents so high that she didn't even want to think about it.

She thought of the offer Kurt had reiterated only last night and without warning her face bloomed a becoming pink with the thoughts that followed. He had woken early and left while it was still dark, giving her a long kiss before regretfully pulling away. He had been so wonderful, so warm, so tender to a novice. She grinned to herself. He had a rich, warm sense of humor and it had shone in the dark as they lay in bed, curled one against the other, and told funny stories about their childhoods and the first loves of their lives before finally falling asleep. He had promised to see her this evening. . . .

The Newstime Tower loomed in front of her and she parked her slightly battered moped in the lot across the street. She might as well splurge and take Gina out for a hot dog. The rest of the day didn't promise to be any brighter than the morning had been. Besides, it was noon and she had to eat sometime.

The marble, plant-decorated lobby was filled with secretaries and reporters, each seemingly carrying out some important job or getting ready to leave for lunch, assignments or both.

"Gina!" she called and the tall lovely girl standing by the elevator turned toward her, a smile shining on her face.

"Victoria! What a surprise! What are you doing here?"

"I've been apartment hunting and I'm at the end of my rope. I thought I'd take pity on you and offer you lunch at Hal's." Her eyes skittered back to the group Gina had been with, seeing one young man whose eyes hadn't left her friend's figure. "But I see you've already made other plans," she teased.

Gina colored. "Well, why don't you join us?" She waved the man over. "Jim, I'd like you to meet my best friend, Victoria Branden Brown. She freelances and writes fiction. Vicky, Jim Henry."

Victoria stuck out her hand. "Hi, Jim. I bet with a name like yours you're always getting double mail," she teased and he laughed easily.

"I'm afraid so. Either way, Jim Henry or Henry Jim," he admitted. "Are you joining us for lunch?"

"Miss Brown doesn't know it, but plans have already been made for her," a deep nerve-tingling voice spoke from behind her.

Victoria didn't have to turn around to know who it was, but she was mesmerized by the look on her friend's face. It was sheer, unadulterated shock.

She hadn't expected to see Kurt until that evening when, she was sure, they would resume their discussion of his townhouse. He had let the subject drop too easily, and she knew he had more to say. Her skin flushed with the other, more intimate thoughts that traveled on the heels of that one. The thought of him holding her close to the lean length of his firm, strong body. The thought of his head bending over her breast as his breath rasped in his throat from their lovemaking.

She turned slowly. "Hi, Kurt. What are you doing here?" She tried not to devour him with her eyes, but it was impossible, just as it was for him.

Gina's voice sounded squeaky. "You know Mr. Morgan, Victoria?"

Confusion ran across Vicky's face before a heavy, doomed feeling settled deep in the pit of her stomach. "Morgan?" she whispered. "Kurt Morgan of *Newstime* magazine. As in 'President'?"

His dark eyes silently tried to reason with her. "The same." He glanced at Gina, then Jim. "If you'll excuse us, I think I have some explaining to do."

"Explaining? Now why would you have to do that, Mr. Morgan? You look like an up-front guy to me," she flashed. "Or are looks as deceiving as I'm thinking they are?"

"There are reasons for everything, Victoria."

"And a time and a place for explanations," she retorted. "And this isn't it!" If she could have gotten away with it she would have punched him in the mouth!

"Then we'll go someplace else. The time is perfect," he said with a finality that would have made a five-star general quake, and marched her out the front door without looking back to see the astonishment plastered on his employees' faces.

"Where's your car?"

"I have the moped today," she snapped between clenched teeth, glancing sideways to take in the cut of his hand-tailored suit. He wasn't just wealthy. He was rich! And rich meant power, and power hurt people. Damn him! Damn him!

She wrenched her arm away. "Leave me alone, *Mr. Morgan*. I don't need your lunch, your help—or your apartment!" she almost shouted as she backed away from him.

"And my lovemaking, Victoria? Do you need that?" He took a step toward her, making her retreat again.

"No!" One hand rose to ward him off, but he continued to pursue her.

"May we discuss this at your apartment? I'm not inclined to make scenes in front of my own employees," he said calmly, and for the first time she realized that the employees of the magazine were milling around the hot pavement, throwing sidelong glances at the two of them.

She waved a dismissive hand in the air. "Forget it, Kurt. I don't want to see you again." With her head held high she crossed the street to the parking lot and picked up her helmet from the attendant, expecting Kurt's heavy hand to fall on her shoulder at any minute. As she gunned the small motor she saw him from the corner of her eye, standing on the pavement, watching her pull out of the lot and down the street. He never even bothered to try to stop her.

By the time she reached her apartment her anger was gone, but not her resolution. She stomped up the stairs to the door, her head down, watching her feet—until she saw another pair of shoes. These were far more expensive than her own and looked to be made of hand-sewn Italian leather.

"That moped has got to go. Do you realize that someone could miss seeing that piece of tin and run you over before they could even brake? I won't have you flirting with death that way." His voice was harsh, cold. When she looked up and realized how furious he was her own anger returned.

"What I do has nothing to do with you." She placed her hands on her hips, her eyes spitting fury. "You may be rich beyond most people's wildest dreams, you may have all the power in the world, but you have no control over me! Ever!" One slim finger pushed against his massive chest. "I don't belong to anyone but myself! I live and let live and I expect you and those like you to do the same! Is that understood?" His face darkened, but she wouldn't heed the warning. "And if I ever decide to belong to someone, it certainly won't be a rich liar!" she shouted.

His strong arms snaked out, crushing her to his chest. "You're insane!" he muttered just before his lips clamped down on hers, branding her with his searing possession.

She wiggled against him as she tried to get loose of his iron hold, but all she accomplished was to make his grip tighten. Finally she sagged against him, her fury gone and the ever-lurking depression replacing it.

When he finally let her go she stared up at him with tear-glistened eyes.

"Don't you see, Kurt? I can't be hemmed in, all tied up in a pretty package like someone's Christmas treat. And you," she almost choked, "you're like all the rest of your kind. You manipulate, seek power over others, steal secrets. . . ." She couldn't tell him that he had stolen her heart. It would only give him another weapon to use against her already weakened resolution.

"We can't talk here. Let's go inside," he commanded firmly, cupping her chin in his hand and looking down at her with tenderness. It was as if he hadn't heard a word she said.

Her shoulders slumped. "There's nothing to discuss," she stated softly, reaching for her keys. "It's over."

But he followed her in anyway, right into the kitchen, where she opened the refrigerator door and poured herself a stiff glass of wine. *"Salud,"* she muttered before gulping down a swallow, feeling the chill and then the heat of it.

"What have you got against being rich, anyway? I know you don't have much, but money doesn't do anything more than pay the bills. It certainly doesn't eliminate problems."

"No, it doesn't. But it does make for more powerful bullies," she said sourly.

"Victoria . . ." He was leaning against the door-jamb, his arms at his sides, looking almost as weary as she was. "Didn't last night mean anything to you?" His voice sounded pleading and she looked at him carefully, trying to steel herself against her own volcanic emotions.

"I think you know how much it meant. But it was a gift, Kurt. Not a weapon for you to use against me."

"I wouldn't do that."

"No?" she questioned. "And what about all the other women in your life? Don't they mean anything to you?"

She had caught him off guard; she could tell by his expression. Suddenly she had the answer she wanted, only now she didn't want it anymore. There already was someone in his life. Victoria, not the other woman, was the extra. Then something else dawned on her.

Her eyes narrowed in speculation. "And what *were* you doing answering an ad in a singles newspaper? Why in the world would the president of a corporation such as yours want to have *another* mistress to clutter his life?"

His hand came out in a pleading gesture. "Victoria . . ."

"Answer me, damn you!" she exclaimed, slapping his hand away and in the process spilling all her wine down his hand-tailored suit.

Her hand covered her throat, eyes big. "I'm sorry,"

she whispered, grabbing a towel and trying ineffectually to dab at his leg.

"Victoria, stop it!" he ordered imperiously, all pleading gone, and she slowly straightened and waited for him to bawl her out. His voice lowered, becoming soothing and tender. "The suit is expendable. You're not. I'll answer your questions one by one. Then perhaps you'll see that I'm not the 'powerful bully' you think I am." He gave a small, sad smile. "But first let me rinse the wine off my pants." He turned toward the bedroom door. "Meanwhile, pour me a glass of that California chablis." His eyes suddenly twinkled, his smile lines deepening. "After all, I love America, too."

A chuckle mixed with unshed tears at the memory of their first date. It stayed there as she turned to answer a knock on her door.

# 5

**∘∘∘∘∘∘∘∘∘∘**

The smile froze, her face paling at the sight of the older, distinguished man standing in the doorway.

"My God," she whispered, backing away. It had been seven years since she had last seen her father. Seven years trying to forget the total heartbreak of ending a relationship that had once been very close to hero worship.

"Hello, princess. May I come in?" He sounded weary and she opened the door wider without even thinking. He followed her into the small but cheery living room, his eyes scanning the room quickly before coming back to rest on her.

"It's been a long time. How have you been?" He stood in the middle of the room, clumsy in his attempt to make conversation.

She nodded, her thoughts whirling in different directions like a leaf in the wind. One particular thought held.

"Is it Mother?" she questioned hoarsely, her nerves taut with strain until he shook his head.

"No. Your mother's no better, but she isn't any worse, either," he admitted.

"Then, why . . . ?"

"I came to see you, princess. I thought we might be able to mend a few fences. Seven years is a long time to punish a father. But in your case, you're punishing a whole family." He sat down heavily in a small chair by the window, his eyes never leaving her face.

Her voice was cold. "Not long enough."

"I know we hurt you, Victoria. It hurt me too. You'll never know how much." He sounded so sad, so tired.

Victoria straightened her spine, stiffening her already tattered emotions against him as well. "Then you'll understand if I don't ask you to stay."

He ignored her words, only a flinch showing the power she had to hurt him. "But you knew before that I had another family. You knew it and accepted it."

"Yes, I knew. What I didn't know was how you thought of them compared to how you thought of us. Your 'real' daughter had the right to call you Dad. Your real daughter didn't have to suffer through an introduction to her sister, hearing herself identified as someone else's child." She turned her back on him and walked to the window. Visibly shaking, she couldn't face him, couldn't let him see the intense pain seven years hadn't erased. "You chose the path I took that day when you disowned me, and you chose again when I ran away and you wouldn't take me back publicly because of the harm the publicity would have done to your career."

"Oh, Victoria." His muttered imprecation seemed

to come from far away. "You were my princess. The only child who loved me without restraint or reason."

"*Was* is the operative word, Senator. I *loved,* I *was.*" She turned to face him, tears valiantly held back. "But it's gone. It seems that loving without reason is a handicap that has no compensations."

"Not even for your mother's sake?" He grasped at straws.

Her voice was hardly a whisper. "Heaven help me, not even for her."

They were both startled to see Kurt standing in the door, sizing up the situation with sharpened eyes. He nodded slightly. "Senator."

"Kurt Morgan," her father answered, straightening in his chair, his eyes traveling between the other man and his daughter. "What are you doing here?"

"The real question, Father, is what are *you* still doing here?" Victoria interjected. "Kurt has been invited."

Both men said her name at the same time, one sharply and one sadly. But she could not back down now. If she backed down her emotions would overtake her and she couldn't stand that. There would be too much pain for her to cope with. She didn't understand what egged her on to speak the next words.

"I don't know how you two know each other, but"—she turned to stare down at her father, her face rigid—"Kurt has asked me to move into his apartment. I've just accepted."

"Victoria! No!" The pain in her father's voice washed over her, but it was too late to stop.

"Yes. I'll be moving next week. Tell Mother I'll let her know my new address."

His shaking hands reached for her, then dropped to his sides. He stared at the younger man. "Don't do this thing, Kurt. Don't." His voice broke.

Kurt stepped forward. "Stephen," he began, only to have Victoria interrupt him.

"You taught me well, Senator. I'm only following in my mother's footsteps. What was good enough for her is good enough for me. Isn't that how every daughter is supposed to feel?"

Slowly her father rose from the chair, finally facing her, torment written all over his face. "Well done, Victoria. You're a regular chip off the old block. I only hope you'll be able to live with yourself later. Sometimes the years don't go fast enough to keep pace with a guilty conscience."

She stood completely still, hands clenched at her sides, holding her breath as she heard the front door close quietly behind him. His footsteps echoed down the hallway, slightly shuffling, an old man's steps. Still she held her breath, staring at the wall, willing herself not to think of the scene just past. She blinked her eyes to keep the events from replaying in her mind, pushing away the gallons of salty tears that threatened to fall.

Kurt never moved. His face was a mask, hiding whatever he thought as he studied the frightened young woman in front of him who was so tormented in her own private hell. After overhearing their conversation so many things—her attitudes, her thoughts— were clear to him now. No wonder his offer had upset her. She was already living with tightly leashed emotions, holding them in check. He watched, afraid of going to her and afraid of staying away. He was afraid for her, period.

"Victoria?" His voice sounded as if he were talking to a child. Slowly, with measured steps, he came toward her to slowly envelop her in his arms. She was stiff, shivering, her eyes never moving to meet his.

"Cry, baby." His voice was rough with emotion. "Rant, rave, scream. Let go. Do something."

And she did. She cried so hard that she couldn't breathe. Her shaking hands clasped his shirt as if it were a lifejacket, her head resting on his shoulder as she sobbed away seven years of grief. She cried for thoughts and words unsaid, and anger unspoken. She cried for the seventeen-year-old who had been hurt and grown up too fast, and the twenty-four-year-old who couldn't leave the pain behind. She cried as she had never cried before and Kurt held her, crooning to her, rocking her in the strength of his arms, protecting her from the world outside. He asked no questions and gave no answers. He was just there.

When he carried her to bed she curled up to him like a kitten, never letting go of his shirt. One arm was wrapped around his neck for human warmth, her body still shivering as if with a chill. Her sobs subsided only when she fell into an exhausted sleep, leaving Kurt awake to hold her, smooth her hair and wonder what the full story behind the scene this afternoon was. Later. He'd find out later. He pulled the comforter up from the foot of the bed, tucking it around them both, then studied the handmade pattern. A wedding ring, flowers, and children dancing in bright vivid colors across a landscape of trees and a meadow. Victoria had made it, he knew, playing out her dreams in fabric instead of reality.

When Victoria finally woke up it was the next afternoon. She could smell coffee perking. She placed a hand on the pillow where Kurt had rested, her fingers finding the hollow his head had made.

She stretched. Her body was sore and aching and it didn't seem to matter that she had slept around the clock. She was still tired. Her brain felt as if it was encased in cotton batting. And she was totally depressed. All night the picture of her father's face had hung behind her closed lids. The sadness in his eyes hurt more than anything else. But that was something she could not, would not, rectify. He had made his bed of pain, and now he could sleep in it. She had.

Kurt's head popped around the door. "Come on, sleepyhead. We've got a busy day ahead of us and need to get a move on."

She gave him a myopic stare, fumbling for her glasses. When she didn't find them in their usual place on the nightstand she gave up, plopping back on the pillow. As she narrowed her eyes to bring him into some kind of focus, Vicky thought she saw him wink, totally at ease. "Coffee's on."

Over ham, scrambled eggs and English muffins he told her of his plans. "First, you're packing a bag and spending the next two or three days at my house in Santa Barbara. Then, when we return, we'll move you into the townhouse. Then we'll begin discussing plans for your parents and yourself." His expression sobered. "No one deserves to pay for a mistake for the rest of their lives, Victoria. Not even your father."

"I won't discuss him with you, Kurt. You're just like he is. One dignified steamroller sympathizes with another. I don't need you in my life, Kurt Who-everyouare!"

"And what will you substitute for me? Your make-believe romances? Nights spent with needle and thread while you sew another dream quilt? Your books and soft music and California wines?"

She glared at him, suddenly feeling the conflicting tug of emotions again having closed off the past.

"Not good enough, Victoria Branden Brown. Not good enough."

Her eyes widened at his use of her full name. He answered her unspoken question. "I've been snooping. You're twenty-four, five-foot-six, one hundred and twenty pounds—which is too skinny—and you were born in Nevada. You have a brother; I can't tell if he's younger or older than you, but the family resemblance is astounding. You write well for the genre; your idea on the dating newspaper exactly coincides with mine, which shows that great minds work the same way. You've been reasonably happy, healthy, too much on your own for too long and you need someone like me in your life to bring organization out of chaos."

"You're insane," she whispered.

"You're mine. Whether you want to call yourself my girlfriend, my mistress, my lover or my friend, it doesn't matter. You'll be all of those wrapped into one."

"Never!" she stated emphatically.

"We'll see," he answered, unconcerned. "Get dressed. We're going for a drive."

"No. Can't you take no for an answer?" She breathed heavily, trying to contain herself. Since she had met him her entire world had gone topsy-turvy, but she would rectify it herself. And the first step would be getting rid of him!

"If you're through eating I'll bundle you in the car just as you are. I don't care if you're dressed or not. I just thought you'd like it better if you were." He wasn't kidding.

"Not to Santa Barbara." There was only so much she could cope with in a day, and yesterday she'd had enough to last her a week.

"Dammit, Victoria, I'm not some pirate about to kidnap and rape you! I'm just taking you for a drive. Get dressed before that overactive imagination of yours goes haywire."

She did as she was told. After pulling on an old and comfortable pair of jeans and a yellow plaid pullover, she tied her hair back in a low ponytail with a green ribbon, slipped her contacts on and packed an overnight case. She was ready before he had even finished sparkling up the kitchen.

"Why have you been renting cars?" she asked later as they were driving down the freeway, ready to take the coastal route to Santa Barbara. The scenery was beautiful. Tall cliffs with modern homes perched on top stood to the right-hand side of the road, while the Pacific Ocean rolled to the left.

"How did you know?" He sounded more surprised than irritated.

"I saw the rental agreement the first time we went out."

"Why didn't you ask me then?"

"Because I just figured your car was in the shop or you were trying to impress me."

"With a two-year-old car?" Amusement tinged his voice.

"I did wonder about that, but who knows what lurks in the minds of tycoons?" she said sarcastically.

"Easy, Victoria, or I might try one of my notorious, powerful bullying tactics on you," he warned. Then, with a deep sigh, he explained as if to a child. "I wanted to get an interview with a girl, not stun her with money."

She giggled, and he joined her in laughter.

They drove in relaxing silence until reaching Malibu, where Vicky became fascinated by the single row of houses beside the road, clinging to what had once been beach but was now nearly under water. Only the top floors were usually visible from the road, but when they turned a curve she could look back and see the glass fronts facing the rolling surf. Today the ocean was calm, but what would it look like when a storm was approaching? she wondered.

"Santa Barbara is further than Malibu, but the view from my home is just as good. You should see the ocean when a storm is brewing far out at sea. It reminds you that you're a very minor part of nature's grand plan." He expressed her own thoughts out loud.

She pushed closer to the door. The closeness of the interior of the car was making her jumpy. On top of all the problems that had arisen yesterday, she still had to deal with Kurt. Every time he was near her, her heart beat faster, her face reddened, her hands became clammy. It was as if she were allergic to him! Think of something else, she told herself, but since the alternatives were just as exhausting, she continued to concentrate on him.

Kurt Morgan was the typical arrogant, powerful male from whom she had always sworn to stay far away. Good looks combined with money usually made men like him callous toward other people's feelings, yet he seemed . . . different.

Her skin warmed as she remembered how gently he had held her in his arms all night and she knew that, no matter what else Kurt was, he wasn't callous.

She steeled herself. But he *was* a womanizer! And somewhere he had a mistress! The guilt on his face had been plain to see yesterday. He hadn't even bothered to deny it. She studied his strong profile, wondering how often he had to do the chasing. She'd bet her next paycheck that it wasn't often. Women probably flocked to him like birds to breadcrumbs. It hurt unbelievably to think of him with another woman, but she steeled herself to face the thought, almost as if it were a form of punishment for her sins. But if he had someone already, then why did he want her? Did he feel some sort of responsibility toward her? Her eyes narrowed. He wasn't trying to get something on her father, was he?

Without thinking she blurted out, "Just how well do you know my father?"

"Not very," he said calmly, as if he had been waiting for that very question. "We've met at various social functions."

"And that's all?"

"I spent the weekend at his home two years ago."

That stunned her. Despite her knowledge of his life, she had never thought of her father's home as being anywhere but with her mother.

One dark brow rose as he quickly eyed her pale complexion. "You've never been there?"

"No, as I'm sure you gathered yesterday. I'm from the wrong half of the family, so to speak."

"That doesn't stop a strong-willed girl from passing by the old homestead."

"Well, yes, I did once. But it was dark and all I saw was a long low ranch house surrounded by a wide expanse of lawn," she admitted.

"That's just what it is. Only the family doesn't live there as much as they used to, except for his daughter, Laurie."

"Where are they?"

"I believe his wife spends most of her time in Washington, D.C. She can't move around much, but in close quarters she's quite the social butterfly."

"Can't move?"

"She's been confined to a wheelchair for the past ten years or so."

Her befogged brain was whirling again, striking out against her own ignorance. She had never wanted to know about that other family and had refused to read about them, to hear about them. Now she saw that her refusal had cost her dearly. It was too much to comprehend all at once. She laid her head back on the seat, closing her eyes in hopes that she would absorb all this before they reached their destination.

Unconnected thoughts ran through her mind. She remembered the time she had broken a bone in her foot in a fall from a horse and for a solid week she had been in a wheelchair. The smallest things had irritated her: the fact that the front of the house had a step that she had never noticed until she tried to wheel herself out the door and fell; the sink was too high for her to get her own glass of water; everyone except her could play volleyball or dance on the patio or reach things on high shelves. She had had to have another pair of hands to do practically everything. But her father had been marvelous. He had spent the entire week at the house, talking, playing chess, making a game out of everything, including showing her the fundamentals of the stock market in the daily paper. Now she knew why she had seen a sadness in his eyes every time he had glanced at that chair. It explained so much.

Ten years was a long time. But his wife's illness had come after he had reentered her mother's life. He had still done the unforgivable.

A hand on her shoulder shook her lightly. Warm, tobacco-scented breath fanned her cheek. "Wake up, princess. We're here," Kurt whispered, inadvertently using the wrong words.

"Don't princess me," she snapped, instantly awake at his use of her father's pet name for her.

"Sorry. Come on. It's time we ate something. I'm

starving and Mrs. Webb, my housekeeper, has a late lunch waiting."

It wasn't until they were out of the car that Victoria had a chance to look at where he had brought her. The house was on the crest of a large, steep hill blanketed with ground-hugging plants that ran all the way down to the valley. It was stucco and redwood, contemporary in design, with enormous double entrance doors.

Forgetting all her arguments against coming, Victoria followed him into the bright interior. The freeform entry extended directly into one of the largest living rooms Vicky had ever seen. She turned slowly, counting at least four different conversation areas, all taking full advantage of the glass walls that afforded a view of the bay and yacht basin.

"Do you pay for that view by the square inch or by the panel?" she asked dryly.

"Be nice and I may give you the plate-glass cost estimates for some light reading this evening." He took her arm, his touch sending sparks shooting through her flesh as he guided her down the single step and into the large room. They turned right and moved down a wide hallway toward what was obviously a kitchen.

"Hello, Mrs. Webb. Are we too late to do justice to your cooking?"

A heavyset, dark-haired woman turned to greet them. "No, sir. It will be ready in five minutes." She glanced at her watch as if to verify the time. It seemed that Kurt Morgan's house was as organized as his business.

"I'll show Miss Brown to her room, then." The placid, blank-faced housekeeper smiled in token agreement before turning back to her space-age stove.

Kurt silently led the way to the other side of the house, guiding her into a small library where a set of stairs reached to the upper level. "There are three bedrooms on this side and two on the other side of the house." He spoke in a light, conversational tone, as if discussing the weather instead of the proximity of their sleeping arrangements.

"Are you sure you have enough rooms?" she replied sweetly as he pushed open the door.

"I only need one, Victoria, when you're around me."

It took her a minute to absorb his words; then a chill went down her spine as his meaning sank into her mind. "In a sow's ear!"

He ignored her outburst as he went to the window and opened the chocolate-brown drapes to reveal the most breathtaking view Vicky had ever seen. Unlike the living room, it looked out over the valley, but slightly to the right, on display like a panorama, she could see the lights of the bay. He opened the window and the scent of the sea drifted in, fresh and clean. Vicky took a deep breath, filling her lungs with it.

"I love it." She turned and looked over the room Kurt had given her. The carpet was a warm tan, the walls tan with white trim. The luxurious bedspread was the true eyecatcher, though. It was a velvet patchwork quilt in shades of brown, accented with dark gold, and it covered an enormous bed. She stared at it, then back up at Kurt. Visions she didn't want to acknowledge danced in her head, bringing life to all her other senses; she remembered the smell of him, the feel of his skin under her palm. . . .

"It's an extra-large king size. Six inches longer and wider than usual. I like lots of space to move around." He could hardly keep the chuckle from his voice.

"And I suppose you expect me to sleep there with you?" Her calves tightened in readiness to run. She eyed the distance to the door. She didn't know where she would go, but she certainly wasn't staying here! What was the matter with her? She had just blithely gone off with a liar and a cheat to become the very thing she had hated all her life! She must have been temporarily insane!

"If that's an invitation, then I accept. If it isn't, then I'll just sleep in my room, next door. But it will have to be one or the other, Victoria. I won't spend another night holding you close to me and not being allowed to stroke or touch. I'm not made of iron when it comes to you." His voice dropped to a husky tone, his eyes warming to blaze over her slim body as he took in her frightened doe-like appearance. "Either way. Your choice. All right?" His mouth quirked into a teasing smile, bringing out the small laugh lines at the corners of his eyes.

Suddenly she let out the breath she had been holding, a sheepish grin replacing her fright. "Thank you," she said softly.

He was suddenly serious once more. "I won't push you, but I want you very much. You know that. When you can admit that you want me just as much, then come to me. Tell me, Victoria. Don't be lonely just because you're afraid of the alternative." He gave a small sad smile. "There may be more alternatives than you know."

By the time Victoria finished lunch she was so tired that her head was drooping. Kurt followed her up to her room, tucked her in with a chaste kiss and closed the curtains and door softly, then went downstairs, where he paced the length of the living room, his head bowed, his hands in his pockets. He had to face a few facts himself.

He couldn't keep the image of Victoria's laughing face from intruding on his thoughts. Her teasing eyes seemed to stare back at him from the depths of the carpet. Her impish smile sought to catch his eye from the shine on the toe of his shoe. She had been so joyous, so full of life the evening she had taught him the fun of video games. He smiled to himself. He had never had such a cheap date. The entire evening hadn't cost what cocktails would have run with Julie, whose reaction when he had told her that things were over had left him in no doubt that his money, not his personality, had been the big attraction for her.

Until last night he hadn't given a thought to not continuing his relationship with Victoria. She was bright, eager for life, fun and totally giving, without seeking something in return.

Then Senator Branden had shown up and Kurt had become enmeshed in a conflict he knew little about. He was now the pawn for Victoria's fantasy of revenge against her very powerful father. Damn! He never should have gotten involved. He was old enough to see trouble and should have stayed clear of this particular brand. He always chose women without expectations, because he certainly had none. He must be slipping.

He had followed through with Margie's suggestion for the fun of it. He'd been behind the desk too long and was suddenly seeking a change—any change that would take him out of the routine he had set for himself.

But never in a million years had he expected to meet a woman like Victoria. And if he *had* expected someone like her, it would have been beyond his wildest imaginings to see himself so drawn to someone so opposite in tastes and lifestyles. He had never believed that opposites attracted. Indeed, he still didn't, but he did know that if she left his life right now there would be a hole, a gap, a chasm that no one could fill. If she left, how long would it take him to replace her? Could she be replaced? He didn't want to hazard a guess. He had become too emotionally involved with her and her problems, and that was usually the kiss of death to a relationship. But not in this case. Instead, he felt protective of her. He wanted to shield her from everyone who could hurt her, including her own father. It was a new feeling for him, one that sat very uncomfortably.

Now what? He wanted her; that was obvious. He enjoyed her company; that was a fact. She was forever surprising him; that she had proven.

And she would not live with him or allow him to care for her.

Why did it matter so much?

The answer was there—all he had to do was say it. His mouth clamped shut. He couldn't; he couldn't take the chance. There would only be pain in it—for both of them.

He rubbed the back of his now stiff neck, stopping to stare out the window. Then he came to a decision.

He would see her through this difficult time, move her into the townhouse and set up the lease with his lawyer so that it would all be aboveboard. Then, slowly, he would bow out of her life. If, while he was helping her rearrange her life, she happened to feel like sharing her bed with him . . . then fine. If not . . . then he would take cold showers.

With the decision made and his life once more in order and under control he should have felt better. Instead he felt only a tearing emptiness when he thought of her bright smile, her trusting tears, her quick mind and the joy he had felt in sharing her bed. What he needed, he thought, laughing mirthlessly, was a shower—now.


Victoria awoke quickly, immediately knowing where she was and why she was there. She sat up, placing both feet on the deep pile of the carpeting and running her soles across it, loving the feeling of the plush softness.

She glanced around, wondering how long she had slept. She wasn't too worried about it, though. In fact, she felt better than she had felt in a long time.

Kurt had done that for her. Kurt had rearranged her life for her, given her a hiatus from decision making and asked nothing in return. Well, she thought again, *demanded* nothing in return. He had *asked* for plenty, but asking wasn't the same as expecting. And because he didn't expect, she could give—freely, wondrously, totally. There were no scorecards, no tallies to keep. She didn't owe him her time or her life or her body. And that was exactly the way she wanted it.

It was strange how much of a burden two people could make out of love. When they loved they also automatically expected and demanded. She knew, had known since yesterday, that she loved Kurt Morgan. But she also knew that she didn't *have* to feel anything for him. She just did.

She heard the sound of rushing water coming from his private bathroom and knew that Kurt must be taking a shower. She almost bounced into his room and opened the bathroom door.

"Kurt?" she called above the sound of the water.

"I'll be out in a minute, Victoria." His voice was muffled by the noise.

"May I join you?" she teased, suddenly so light-hearted that she wanted to hug herself . . . or him.

"No! I'll be there in just a minute. Wait outside!"

She could see him through the milky glass of the door. He was magnificent.

"I think I'll join you after all," she said, opening the shower door with a click. But his hand snaked out and pulled it shut, again keeping her on the other side.

"Stop it, Vicky! How much do you think I can take?" he shouted, at the end of his temper.

"Not much more, I hope." She chuckled, not at all dismayed by his anger. "Why can't I join you?" She had to share her love with him, though she couldn't bring herself to speak of it. Why couldn't he see that?

"Don't tease." His voice was gruff with emotion, his anger dissolving as he opened the door a crack and stared down at her, his heart tightening at what his eyes saw.

The laughter left her voice. "I'm not teasing, Kurt." She pulled the door completely open and stepped in, clothing and all.

"Don't, Victoria! You'll get wet!"

"Isn't that what showers are for?" she asked, taking the bar of soap from his hand and turning him around. She rubbed in a circle, making a wealth of lather on his back, her hand occasionally making a teasing foray down his spine to rest at the base of his trim hips before once more slipping up his broad back to pay attention to his shoulders.

He stood perfectly still, his head tilted so that the water cascaded down his neck and shoulders.

"Turn around," she ordered huskily and he faced her, emitting a low groan from deep in his throat as he stared at her. The warm water had molded the thin fabric of her shirt to the uplifted tilt of her firmly peaked breasts.

"Don't you ever wear a bra?" he ground out hoarsely.

"Not if I can help it." She grinned slowly and glanced at him through her lashes. "Most men don't notice."

"I noticed. I noticed the first time I saw you." One hand came up and gently cupped her breast before reaching to her shirt hem and tugging it over her head.

Her long hair turned darker in the water, her head held proudly as she watched him devour her with his eyes.

All she had left were her jeans. His hands moved and within moments he was throwing them over the shower door.

He leaned against the far wall. He was still afraid she was teasing and didn't realize what she was promising. She was a free spirit, an elusive wraith. "Do you know what you're doing, Victoria?"

An impish grin lit her face. "To you? Yes. I think that's fairly obvious."

One hand came up to soap his chest, her other hand following to feel the sinew and muscles and strength of him, reveling in the symmetrical masculinity of his body. He was brawny and tall and tough. But he was also kind and gentle and sweet. He was a mass of wonderful contradictions.

"Men are so different." She spoke her thoughts out loud.

"Women are different," he corrected. "You most of all." He still didn't reach out and touch her, and in the waiting her need for him grew stronger. Her senses were tuned to him, to every nuance of words, breath, body. Her insides were trembling in anticipation of his touch.

"Do you want to make love to me?" Her honest eyes locked with his, willing him to respond.

"Yes." His voice was so low that it broke.

"Then what are you waiting for?"

"My turn. Give me the soap."

He began at her throat, massaging the sides of her

neck, his thumb finding the hollow where the pulse beat. He placed a stray strand of hair carefully behind her ear and began on her slim shoulders, under her arms, down her arms to her wrists, palms and then each finger. He paid careful attention to each part of her, soaping her skin, holding her arm under the warm jet of water, then soaping another area. His hands caressed her in an almost impersonal way, but his eyes told her of his ultimate goal. Her breasts were cleaned one at a time. He paid particular attention to the undersides, cupping and teasing them with the softness of a breath.

Her eyes never left his face, watching thoughts of things to come flit across his features. She stood obediently still, waiting for him to finish his task.

His hands traveled to her waist, then hips, the soap lathering to a rich creamy foam. Ever so slowly he lathered her long legs, caressing, stroking, teasing as he went, and an urgency built in her. The blood of excitement pounded in her head, shutting out the sound of the hissing water.

"Now?" she questioned, her eyes begging.

"Wait," he ordered softly, continuing on his chosen path.

He bent down, his face level with her slim waist, lathering the backs of her knees, her calves. Then he lifted one foot and soaped it. He followed the same pattern he had performed on her hands and arms, his touch now an agonizingly painful pleasure. When he finished he stared up at her, a grim smile on his mouth.

"Rinse off," he commanded in a low, burlap-rough

voice, and she automatically took a step forward into the water's spray and closer to him. His head tilted up, his chocolate-brown eyes never leaving her face, watching her reaction to his tantalizingly intimate touch.

She moaned, a primitive, animal sound that came from deep within, and still the brown velvety softness of his eyes kept her glued to the spot. Her breathing became short, whispery, her face flushed from his gentle yet persistent efforts. Her mind was a spinning vortex of feelings, with heat flooding her body until she thought she was on fire. And still he continued. His knowing hands crept up her slim legs to softly knead her buttocks, slippery with the clean-scented soap and water, then drifted on, only to linger on another part of her flesh. Silken touches, stroking everywhere, made her aware of the deep stirrings he created to bring her closer to the tall cliffs of ecstasy waiting just beyond the next touch. A persistent tingling poured through her veins, warmth rushing all through her, vibrating her with its intensity and turning her bones to golden liquid honey. Her eyes grew wide with wonder, her lips softening into a small secret smile as she watched him continue his ministrations. Then suddenly she could take no more.

"Kurt!" she cried. And still he kept on, holding her upright with his powerful arms as she swayed and swirled through a mist of unbelievable rainbow colors and crashing sounds.

Her nails were embedded in his shoulders, her head lolled forward as she caught her breath. He stood and held her to his lean tanned body as she slowly found her way back from the heaven he had created for her. His heart was beating a double-time tattoo in her ear. His desire was still strong.

She arched her back and looked up into his loving face. "Your turn," she whispered.

"Our turn," he stated softly. "But first I get to dry you off."

When they entered the bedroom she saw that the drapes were open to let the room fill with the spectacularly colored sunset. The huge bed was soft but firm. The sheets were silken and slippery. Victoria loved it. She watched Kurt walk across the carpet toward her and marveled at his magnificent build. At least for a while he was hers, and nothing made her world as complete as this man could.

Bodies close, skin touching skin, tasting, feeling, sensing, being. It was marvelous.

Sated, completely content, Kurt curled Victoria to him, her small trim hips cupped in front of his, his hands staking proprietary claim to her breasts. He stared down at her still dampened hair, marveling at this wonderful, giving woman who enjoyed pleasing him as much as he did her, and thanked fate for bringing them together. His eyes were still shining in wonder as he slowly closed them and relaxed against her. They slept the late afternoon sun away.

Victoria opened her eyes and focused on Kurt's face in repose. She longed to stroke his chin, kiss his sleeping eyelids. She wanted to thank him. But most of all she wanted to tell him of her deep love.

She smiled to herself, remembering the tender kisses and giving hands that had explored her body.

He must certainly feel something for her or he never would have become involved with her as deeply as he was. No man disrupted his orderly way of life without reason. She sensed that no matter how many mistresses, past or present, he had known, he had opened himself to none of them as he had to her.

She frowned. But if he didn't love her, what was his reason? He had once said that making love and love weren't the same things. He could do one but not the other. Was he only feeling sorry for her? That idea brought a searing pain to her breast and she resolutely pushed her mind away from that thought.

She eased her slim form from under his arm and sat up, carefully swinging her feet to the floor. She'd find her overnight case and clean up before waking him. As she came around the bed to Kurt's side she leaned down and placed a light kiss on his brow, wishing him well until she returned.

Her case was in her bathroom. One pair of jeans and another shirt, both dry, and a meager assortment of cosmetics were all she had brought. Suddenly she wished she had the glamorous accouterments other women used to make themselves beautiful for their men. She wanted to look as wonderful outside as she felt inside. After giving her long hair a good brushing, then braiding it in a long rope down her back to keep it from getting unruly, she applied mascara to her lashes and clear gloss to her lips. That was the best she was capable of doing.

When she was done she simply sat and thought. She loved him, but what did that mean? Her love was so confusing, leaving her up in the clouds one minute, cast down the next. He was so frightening in the way he took charge of her life. And she, after the horror of her parents' relationship, was terrified of trusting. She loved him, but when all was said and done, she didn't want to. Even if he loved her, or thought he did, it could make no difference to the future. In the end she would be alone.

Kurt listened to the muted sounds coming from her bathroom, his eyes closed. He had been awake longer than Victoria, but hadn't wanted to break the closeness between them. He hadn't wanted to admit to it, either. It frightened him.

He had never felt so penned in, so close to a woman before, and this new feeling took getting used to. What was it about her that made her so special to him? She had a good figure, but not fantastic. Her pert nose, stubborn chin and wide eyes were attractive, but hardly classically beautiful. Her disorganized lifestyle and unorthodox background weren't what he was used to or wanted for himself.

Then why was he lying here like a lovesick calf, eagerly waiting for her return? He jumped up, vigorously grabbing at the clothing in his closet, tearing his shirt and jeans off the now swinging hangers.

Suddenly he was angry. She had no right to tie him in knots like this! His life had been just the way he wanted it before she floated in and it could damn well be that way again! In fact, he wanted it that way again, he told himself, ignoring the knowledge that it was his very desire for a change that had led to meeting Vicky in the first place. He wasn't going to lie around waiting for her to come to him on his terms when he had plenty of other women he could go to. She certainly wasn't the only one. There were women all over the place, crawling out of every country club and town-house in America. Why one woman with a passion for quarter-a-throw video games and hot dogs at mid-night could crawl under his skin was beyond explana-tion!

Then he smiled with self-knowledge. Who was he kidding? He knew just how he felt about Vicky, even if he didn't know why, and he knew exactly what to do about it.

# 6

⌒⌒⌒⌒⌒⌒⌒⌒⌒

No! I *don't* understand!" Kurt ran an agitated hand through his hair as he stared in bewildered anger at the slim bit of highhanded woman in front of him. Her breasts rose and fell in extreme anger, her eyes alive with rage. "For the life of me I can't see anything insulting about our getting married!"

"That's what I mean! You can't even begin to understand my viewpoint!" she stormed, her hands clenched at her sides, almost visibly restrained, as if she would love to shake him thoroughly. "You're trying to take over my life! I walk in here and find you on the phone, okaying the removal of *my* possessions from *my* apartment, as if you owned me! I told you I would move, but I didn't mean that you could take over. I'll move when *I'm* ready, not when you are!"

"Is that what this is about? Me moving you out of an apartment you needed to move from and into an apartment that you had already agreed you would occupy?" He looked almost relieved, as if he could understand a woman's illogical mind much better than she could, and her anger built up even further.

She took a deep breath, reminding herself that he was trying to be tolerant while she was giving an explanation she knew he would never understand.

"You're asking me to become a part of you," she said in a barely controlled voice. "You want to protect me." He nodded as if relieved that at least she understood that. But her next words dampened any hope he might have had. "You want to wrap me in cotton and put me in a box that only you can open when it pleases you. I cannot, *will* not, do that!"

"That's not what I'm trying to do. I just proposed to you, asked you to marry me! How in the hell could I know you'd take it as an insult?" he shouted.

"I didn't! It was just that added to all the other things you do, it was too much! Can't you see that?" She stamped her foot in frustration before turning toward the window and staring sightlessly out at the purple-tinged night.

When her emotions had calmed down a bit, Kurt spoke. "I'm in a position to take care of your needs. Is that so bad?" His voice was a low caress as he stood directly behind her, not touching her physically, but stroking her with his tone. "I find it hard to believe, but I love you. Most men want to cherish the woman of their dreams." His hands slipped around her waist and eased up to cup her breasts, his thumbs erotically stimulating her nipples. She leaned back, succumbing to his spoken thoughts. When he said the words they didn't seem so much possessive as loving. She had to force herself to see the controlling side of him, to remember the pain, the betrayal that went with the loving.

"If you decide that you want to make a career out of writing, that's fine. I don't mind. You can do whatever makes you happy." Her spine stiffened. She turned in his arms and stared up at his puzzled face, the frown marks making deep grooves in his forehead as his dark eyes searched hers for an answer.

"That's just it, Kurt. I don't need your permission to do whatever I want, just as you don't need to ask mine to continue with your business."

His look was startled. "Why would I ask you if I could continue with my business? It's my livelihood."

"And if you were just beginning? If your company wasn't making money? What then?" she persisted, trying to keep her arms at her sides instead of twining them around his neck.

"Then I'd keep at it, but I wouldn't ask you to marry me until I could support us." His grin was lopsided and totally endearing. "I'd ask you to live with me instead," he joked, trying unsuccessfully to lighten the mood.

"But you're not giving me the same freedom. You're being kind by allowing me to continue with what I've already chosen to do, tolerating my career, while you expect what you've decided to do with your life to take precedence."

Kurt heaved a sigh. "I'm not sure I understand, Victoria, but if you explain very slowly and simply, perhaps we can come up with a compromise that will work for both of us. Right now you've got me confused and on the verge of anger. I've never heard of a woman turning down a proposal because the man didn't ask her permission to continue with his career."

Her eyes glistened with tears that she refused to shed. "Please don't patronize me, Kurt."

He swallowed hard at the obvious pain and frustration etched on her face and gave her a swift hug. "You're right." He led her to the rumpled bed and sat her down, placing himself next to her as he continued to hold her hands. "Now explain, slowly."

She swallowed hard several times before she could speak. How could she make him understand, with simple words, the emotions that were so complex and deeply affecting? "When I was young I idolized my father and, in turn, he wrapped me up in cotton batting, Kurt. Because he wasn't always there he tended to make sure that Mother did the same as he did: protecting, cosseting, shielding me from life. I got into the habit of pleasing him instead of pleasing me. Do this, choose that, act this way. But there was always the implication that if I didn't do what he wanted, then he wouldn't love and take care of me." She smiled sadly at the thought of those lost years. They seemed to belong to someone else's lifetime. "At that age I couldn't bear to have his love withdrawn, so I did as I was supposed to, secure in the knowledge that as long as I did he would smile, protect and be proud of me. But it didn't work out that way. I was living, believing, in a lie. When reality hit me on the head I wasn't prepared for it and it almost totaled me. I was forced to learn how to survive, to take care of myself, to make my own way in the world without another person's help. I had to be responsible for my own actions and no longer blame my faults on others.

I've learned how to be myself now and I *can't* give that up!" She took a deep breath before continuing. "And you, Kurt, are trying to place me in that same little niche that my father wanted me to live in. You're attempting to take me over in the same way. Don't you see?" Her voice was a plea as she stared into his eyes, begging him to understand the depth of her emotions. But all she saw was distance and something else that she couldn't name.

The silence was deafening. "You still don't understand." Her voice was a mere whisper.

"Probably more than you know, Vicky," was his quiet answer. Sadness flickered across his face before he stood and pulled her up with him, right into his arms. "You were more than I bargained for when I made that first date," he teased, but his voice was hoarse with unsaid emotions. He stroked her hair and they stood in the darkened room, each listening to the other's heartbeat and wondering how to reach the one they loved. They said nothing, seeing no way across the chasm that separated them.

Dinner was quiet. The tense anger of their earlier argument was gone, total exhaustion left as debris. Victoria could hardly lift her fork without forcing herself to do so. When dinner was over they walked through the living room and outside, Kurt leading her to one of the padded lounges on the deck that hung out into space. The stars filled the dark spaces in the heavens; the breeze held just a hint of salt; the night was balmy, neither too hot nor too chilly.

She leaned her head back and closed her eyes, wanting to cry but not knowing which of the many reasons she should choose to cry about. She felt totally drained.

The clink of ice against crystal told her that Kurt was fixing drinks, and when he placed a glass in her hand she obediently sipped. It was an almond liquor over ice and tasted both fresh and cool. Kurt took the lounge next to hers, his free hand closing to hold hers tight, his fingers playing with her palm, and his voice broke the silence. "Victoria, I still want you to marry me, but I'm willing to wait until you feel you can trust me."

"I trust you now." Her hand tightened on his as she spoke words she knew were a lie. The simple truth was that she wanted to trust him but didn't.

"No, you don't. You're confusing me with your father."

"I know the difference," she said dryly, trying to ignore the doubts that filled her mind.

"I wish you did."

"I do!" she exclaimed, opening her eyes to stare into the dark depths of his.

"If you did, darling, then you wouldn't automatically accuse me of manipulating you the way he did. You wouldn't be terrified of trusting me, as you are of him. You would take me as an individual." His voice was sad.

"Perhaps you're right. I don't know." Once more inertia took over and she closed her eyes.

"Live with me. See if we can work it out." She

could feel the muscles in his arm tense and was astounded to realize how much her answer meant to him. "Don't make the decision tonight. Wait until tomorrow, so you can be sure you weren't maneuvered into it."

Slowly, gazing at him, she nodded her head in agreement. Hope that they would find a common meeting ground rose in her, fleetingly destroying the deep depression she was wallowing in.

Somehow, even though Kurt had given her back her freedom, she felt confused and torn. She remembered his tall, muscled body in the shower with the soap lathered over him, the rippling muscles, the raw strength beneath her fingertips, the pressure of his possession and the ecstasy of his touch. And now he had given her back that which she thought she had lost: her freedom. He had taken away the ties she was so afraid of being bound with. He was willing to accept her rules once again; he was trusting her, she thought in amazement.

She took another sip of her drink. Was freedom more binding than marriage? Was love always more painful than one could ever imagine? she wondered, closing her eyes and letting her tiredness overcome her. She slept.

Victoria didn't feel Kurt take the glass from her hand, nor did she feel him lift and carry her to the bedroom, where he slipped her clothing off and covered her with the cool silken sheets. All she knew was that she was safe.

Berating himself for a fool, Kurt slid in next to the

small dark-haired girl who turned to him in her sleep for comfort. His arms went around her body to hold her closer and he tried desperately not to touch her rounded breasts, where his hands really wanted to be. A low moan escaped his lips as he smelled the clean scent of her hair and felt the satin-smooth skin of the wriggling body that nestled cozily so close to his. For one wild moment he imagined making his needs known. The memory of that afternoon flashed through his mind. She had been so spirited, so uninhibited, so fresh and wild and wonderful in her own innocent way. She was like no one Kurt had ever known, giving of herself totally in a way that no woman had ever done with him. He wanted to crush her to him and allow them to edge toward the completeness he ached for. But reason returned and he wrenched his hand away from her thigh to close in a fist. It was going to be a long night.

He awoke to find her bending over him, her long hair a dark cloud about her head. Her face was solemn as she continued to stare at him, her eyes wide and sad.

"Good morning." She leaned down and gave him a chaste kiss on his slightly open mouth. "I thought you'd never wake up."

His mood matched hers. "I didn't get to sleep until late."

"Did I keep you awake?"

"Yes." There was a wealth of meaning in that one word.

Slowly she nodded her head in understanding. "I

know. I woke up in the middle of the night and debated on whether or not I should wake you."

It was his turn to be surprised. "Why didn't you?"

"Because I was afraid you might reject my advances," she stated simply. "I want you too much to have you refuse me."

His dark brown eyes turned to velvet, a small smile tugging at his mouth. "Have I turned you into a sex maniac in one short day?"

Suddenly she giggled, a light sound that played across his nerves and heightened his senses. "Yes." Then, in a softer voice, "I never knew. . . ." Her voice faltered.

He gave her waist a light squeeze before his hands traveled down the length of her body. "I know. Neither did I."

"You? But you're a man of the world. Surely the other day wasn't your first time!"

"It was with you." His lips nipped her neck as he breathed in the scent of her.

"What a lovely thing to say."

"The truth is always lovely."

"Even when you don't want to hear it?" she questioned, tensing, knowing that she was going to tell him her answer and he wasn't going to like it.

"Even when I don't want to hear it. If you don't tell me the truth, how will I ever know what you want?" He regarded her soberly. "I need to know your thoughts, Victoria, or we can never go any further than we are today." He heard himself utter the words, but it was hard to believe he had said them. He had never been so open with a woman before. He had never wanted to. Deep inside his stomach clenched with nerves. He knew what she was going to say, and all he could do was delay the moment of truth. Her hand stroked the sun streaks in his hair, her eyes clouding over as his tongue made erotic patterns on her neck. "Kurt . . ."

"Not yet, Victoria. Not yet," he muttered, urgency pounding through his veins as he realized just how close he was to losing her. "Love me, Vicky. I need you."

And she did, telling him with her hands, her tongue and her quiet cries, just how much she loved him. But love was not a cure-all, and in the aftermath of passion reality was still waiting in the wings for its time on center stage.

She was entwined with his body, her head resting on his chest as she listened to the slowing pattern of his heartbeat. She ruffled the hair on his chest.

"I can't live with you, you know."

"I know." His voice was tired, as if he too had wrestled with the problem. "But you're still moving into the townhouse. I'll change your mind in time, Victoria. Someday soon you'll see that being married to me isn't the same as being tied to a life of subjugation and fear, fear of being yourself and losing the one you love. I love you as you are, Vicky. Someday you'll see that. You can be your own person just as well with me as without me. I'll prove it to you, somehow." She wasn't sure if he made the promise to her or to himself, but it was as solemn as a vow.

Breakfast was served on the patio, where they both

reveled in the unexpected early morning sunshine, worshiping it with their bathing-suit-clad bodies.

By lunchtime the air was filled with the intangible electricity that traveled between them. By dinner they were hardly speaking, saying more with their eyes than could ever be spoken aloud. Messages flew through the air, breathing was short and shallow, as each tried not to touch the other for fear of never being able to let go.

Victoria savored him with her eyes, her emotions drawn so that she thought she would scream with the exquisite agony of it. Still he made no advance, and she couldn't.

They stared at the stars over an after-dinner drink. The silence was deafening.

Kurt was the first to break the quiet. "I'll take you to the townhouse tomorrow. Your things were moved today."

"And the rent?"

"The same as we discussed."

"And you?" Her voice was barely a whisper.

He didn't pretend to misunderstand. "I'll be within reach of the phone."

"For how long, I wonder?" she mused aloud, sadness enveloping her. Was she crazy to turn away the one man she had ever loved? Her heart said yes, but a hidden fear in her continued to yell "No!"

"As long as it takes." His voice was grim and a shiver ran down her spine.

"And after tomorrow? When will I see you again?"

"Any time you pick up the phone and ask me to come."

"Why are you doing this? Why can't we be like we were last night? Why must you put strings on me?"

"Because I can't hold you, love you and then let you go. You have to learn to take me as I am. You must make the commitment, Victoria. I've already made my feelings known to you."

"You may change your mind." She knew he was right in not pressing her to come to his bed, yet, perversely, that was exactly what she wanted him to do.

"I won't change my mind. As soon as you realize the importance of 'us' and the difference that it makes I'll be there for you."

Once again she was confused. He spoke sense; he seemed so honest and loving. Yet all her upbringing told her that she would lose herself in him, his work, his thoughts, his ideals. She couldn't lose herself now. She just couldn't! She couldn't take the chance of following in her mother's footsteps, to find out later that she had to part from him before she could be herself or, worse yet, to find out that she could never be the woman he wanted, the woman he needed— and end up living in a horrible limbo, spending her life both with and without him.

The moment Kurt unlocked the townhouse, Victoria was in love. It was sunny and warm and the rooms had a look of individuality, of homeness. The kitchen was large enough to work in but not too large for coziness. The bedroom was a huge loft with a balcony overlooking half the living room. Her furniture was worn, but somehow it looked just as warm and comfortable here as it had in her uncle's apartment.

"I love it!" She squeezed her arms around her middle and danced around the large room before throwing herself into his arms. Then she backed quickly away.

His smile was forced. "I'm glad." He waved toward the phone. "On the underside of the phone is my private line at work and the house phone in Santa Barbara. The rest is up to you." He walked to the coffee table and threw down the key. She could tell by his stride that he was angry and suddenly so was she.

"And do you have a matching set?" Her voice was a sneer.

"Of course. After all, you're renting this property, remember? A good rental agent always keeps a spare set of keys."

"Of course." Suddenly her anger was gone and dejection took its place.

Kurt walked toward the door, his hand on the knob before he spoke again. "There's an art show I'm supposed to attend next week. Will you allow me to escort you?"

"Yes." She turned and walked toward the kitchen. Her back was to him, so he couldn't see the bright light of anticipation in her eyes. "When and where?"

"Next Friday. Eight o'clock."

"I'll be ready."

Then he was gone.

"I really love you, you know," she told the empty room, wishing he was still there and holding her in his arms. She had been alone most of her adult life and she had always loved her solitude. Until now. Suddenly she hated it.

It took her exactly four days to get her new home in shape and return to her regular writing schedule. Another week and Victoria's article on the *Anderson Report* would be completed, though without any dark and dangerous revelations. It was in rough draft and all she had to do was polish it up and put it through the typewriter once more.

Gina came by one evening and celebrated her new surroundings with her, not mentioning Kurt, but her eyes were full of questions which Victoria couldn't answer. It was a stilted evening, with both friends avoiding the one thing on both their minds.

When Friday night finally came Victoria spent more time than she ever had before in getting ready for her date with Kurt. She hadn't had the nerve to call him and he certainly hadn't tried to call her. She knew because she had only left the house twice that week, and both times were late at night to grocery shop at one of the all-night stores down the street.

Victoria's eyes consumed Kurt as he stood in the doorway of the townhouse. He was wearing a white tuxedo jacket with black dress pants that clung to his muscled hips and thighs.

"You're not getting enough sleep." His eyes narrowed on the purplish rings beneath her eyes.

"And you are?" she retorted, noticing the puffiness under his own.

"I drank too much last night," was his excuse.

"And I worked late last night." Anything but the

truth. Why should she explain that her nights were filled with erotic thoughts of him? That a pillow doubled for his long lean body pressed next to hers? That Gina had confirmed the rumors of his starlet mistress, though her presence hadn't been noticed lately, and thoughts of them together were tearing her insides apart? All she had to do was tell him yes and she could have him . . . on his terms. Her mouth tightened into a grim line to keep herself from admitting the truth. After five days she was ready to have him on any terms, and that knowledge frightened her half to death.

They stayed far apart as they walked down the front sidewalk and toward the car. She slipped into the Mercedes without his help. Not a meaningful word was said, but the same electricity was there, charging the air they breathed. Small talk was the order of the day and, although stilted, it gave them a chance to hear each other's voices. She had never been so starved for him before and listened intently to catch anything he said.

The art show was avant-garde, with all the California society notables there, sipping champagne, making polite sounds of delight at seeing each other and ahhing over pictures they didn't understand. And if the pictures hadn't been labeled, neither would Victoria. One was red and black and white and labeled "Anger," while another was three blobs of blue on a soft green background entitled "Tranquility."

Kurt introduced her to a few of the other guests before being called away for a few minutes. Victoria slowly circled the room alone, stopping in front of each painting and pretending an intense interest, when in reality her senses were tuned to Kurt as he held a conversation first with a young couple, then with a beautiful blonde woman who oozed sex appeal from every perfumed pore. Her long red talons rested possessively on his jacketed arm for all of ten minutes before he finally shook her off, reluctantly, it seemed to Victoria, and returned to her side.

"What do you think?" Kurt murmured in her ear. She wasn't quite sure if he was discussing the paintings or the people.

"It stinks." She said it more for shock value than anything else. If he wanted platitudes he could return to the blonde.

His head tilted back and he laughed, a hearty sound that drew attention. His eyes crinkled at the corners as he looked down at her. "I swear, if I was with anyone besides you I'd be shocked by such irreverent talk. But with you, it seems right."

She grinned back. Suddenly the stiltedness was gone, replaced by a warm intimacy. "I just thought I'd shake you up. You're too stiff."

"How right you are," he murmured wickedly, a glint in his eye as he took her arm and began walking slowly about the edge of the room. A thrill ran down her arm at his touch and she shivered. He felt it and his eyes narrowed as he looked at her.

"Miss me? I missed you like hell."

"So did I."

"Another friend? Darling, do you collect women or is it an occupational hazard of the publishing world?"

The tall blonde stood in front of them, almost blocking the way, belligerence written across her features.

"Sometimes I'm not sure. Julie, meet Victoria." His voice was easy, but without intimacy. Victoria smiled, receiving a cold smile in return. Without a word they both knew they were hunters after the same quarry. But Victoria didn't want what Kurt had to offer, did she?

"And do you write also, Victoria?"

"Of course." She returned Julie's smile with even less warmth.

"I see. Do you work for Kurt's magazine?"

"Not yet." She glanced up at the man in question to find him enjoying the altercation. In fact he was enjoying it so much that he was grinning from ear to ear! Damn him!

"How nice," Julie said with obvious falsity. "Well," she said, turning her attention to Kurt, "time for me to go. I'll see you tomorrow, darling. Don't forget, breakfast at ten," she murmured as she walked off.

"Your mistress, I presume?" Victoria's eyes flashed, her voice higher than usual.

"Does it bother you?" Kurt was unruffled; in fact, he was still smiling. "I am, as you may have noticed, looking for a replacement—or a wife. Do you know anyone who's willing to fill that spot?"

"It sounds like just anybody would do. You don't seem to be too choosy with your favors." Her heart was thumping madly against her breast. Knowing someone existed was one thing, meeting her face to face another! He had proposed to her while he was still seeing someone else! What nerve!

"Actually, I'm extremely choosy. There's only one qualification I look for."

"Oh?" She strained to act unconcerned. "And that is . . . ?"

"I think we've had this discussion before," he murmured quietly before reaching to shake hands with a man who had just walked up to them. "Hi, Bob, how have you been?" From that point until they left they had no further chance to talk privately.

The drive home brought more of the small talk that had filled most of the evening. They spoke of the people who had been there, the paintings, even the champagne that had been served.

"Would you like a cup of coffee?" she asked as they drew up to her front door. "I also have some two-day-old danish to challenge your teeth."

He smiled. "I'd like that."

Once they were inside Victoria reached for the light switch, but Kurt stopped her.

"Keep it off. Let me hold you. Let me know you're really here." Her arms looped around his neck, her head tilting, her soft lips unerringly finding his warm, firm mouth. A low groan escaped him before he deepened the kiss, holding her tightly against him as if she would disappear any second. "Why, Victoria? Why are you doing this to us?"

She shook her head, confused thoughts tumbling one over the other. When she was in his arms all rational ideas flitted away on gossamer wings.

His hands traveled over her slender body, searching, searing in their quest. She didn't care that he was fanning a fire that would soon be out of control. Kurt was all that mattered. His lips traced a pattern down the side of her cheek to the small throbbing spot at the base of her throat, searing a path that flooded warmth through her veins like heated lava. She could hardly stand, her legs were quivering so. All the electricity that had sparked between them during the evening had been let loose, the switch pulled to allow it to crackle from one to the other, burning, lighting them with unbelievable frenzy. And then the telephone rang. It didn't register in Victoria's ears at first, but she felt Kurt stiffen; then his hands dropped to his sides.

"Who would call you this late?" he growled. "Another lover?"

"Yes. After losing my virginity with you last week I decided to try everyone, so I went on a prowling binge for the past four days!" she snapped, flipping on the light and turning away so he wouldn't see the hurt his words had caused. But his hand on her shoulder stopped her from moving toward the phone.

"I'm sorry."

"No more than I am." Her throat had a large lump in it as she reached for the phone. "Hello?" Her voice was sharp.

"Victoria? I've been trying to reach you all night. I need to talk to you." Her father's voice came across the wire, tired and dejected, as if he were exhausted.

"I don't think so."

"I do." Suddenly his tone took on purpose. "And I mean to see you. Now, where will it be? At your place or at my hotel?"

"Call me tomorrow and we'll discuss it."

"I'll be right there. I don't care what time it is, I'm going to see you."

"No! Wait!" Suddenly she was alert again, and a sense of danger flooded through her veins. Her father wasn't a man to be dismissed easily. "All right. I'll meet you for lunch tomorrow."

He calmed down slightly and they made the arrangements. After she had hung up Kurt still stood by the door, his jacket open, one hand in his pocket. He looked like an ad for good liquor in a slick men's magazine. His brows came together in a frown that her hands itched to wipe away. "I gather that you're meeting your father?"

"Yes." Her voice was soft, her mind completely occupied with the next day.

"Would you like me to go with you?"

"No. I'll handle him myself." Her voice held a thread of steel.

Kurt continued to persist. "He's probably upset because of your living arrangements, and I don't want you to have to face his accusations alone. After all, you moved here because of me."

"I don't need someone to hide behind when it comes to talking to my father."

"No." His voice turned bitter. "And you don't want anyone, either, do you?"

"I can take care of myself." She sounded like a small, belligerent child, bolstering herself with her own words.

"Of course you can. That's why you spent the

weekend at my house, in my bed. That's why you turned down my proposal of marriage. That's why you were so jealous tonight when you met Julie." He almost trembled with anger. "You're a child, Victoria. A spoiled, frightened child who can't even see the mess she's making out of her life. And all because your past is getting twisted up with your present."

"It's *my* past and *my* present!" she cried, stiffening in anger.

"That's right, it is. You won't let anyone else into your little world. You're afraid to live, to take a chance of someone hurting you. That's why you won't commit yourself to me, why you've refused to see your family again. You're afraid!"

"Get out of here, Kurt Morgan, and don't ever come back." Her voice was low, filled with pain. "I don't ever want to see you again."

He shook his head, the look in his deep brown eyes one of sadness. "Someday . . ."

"There'll be no someday. You just don't understand me."

"I understand you well enough, Victoria. It's you who won't try to see anything but what you want to see."

"Get out."

"For good, Vicky? Or until you realize just what we have going for us?" His dark eyes probed hers, his expression grim and accusing. She stared down at the carpet, unable to hold his look, unable to answer.

"I see. Goodbye, then, my Victoria."

"I'm not yours!"

"You'll always be mine. You just don't know it yet."

And before she could scream her answer at him he was gone.

# 7

~~~~~~~~~~~~~~

**F**or the luncheon with her father Victoria mutinously dressed in a way she knew he would dislike. She wore a white and blue peasant blouse tucked into a long, faded, blue denim skirt and tall brown western boots, and tied her sleek, long dark hair back in a ponytail. Long silver earrings dangled almost to her shoulders. She looked properly rebellious, no doubt exactly what her father expected from her. She went to put in her contacts but decided against them, placing her large, round glasses on the perch of her small nose. There, *now* let him compare her to his other daughter.

The restaurant was a new one, crowded, but not overly so. She spotted him immediately, sitting quietly at a table as he stared into space, his expression sad and tired, confirming that the sound of his voice on the telephone last night had not been an act.

"Hello, Senator." Her voice was soft. She immediately wished she had been more discreet in her choice of dress. It seemed so juvenile all of a sudden.

His eyes lit up as he stood, motioning her into the

seat across from him. "I'm glad you came," he said simply. "I thought you might have changed your mind."

"And what would you have done?"

"Come after you. You're my daughter."

"Really?" Suddenly the anger and hurt were back, bombarding her nerves. "What a shame you just realized it. We could have had such good times together."

He wasn't put off. "We did have good times together. You must have forgotten."

"*I* didn't. *You* did," she said with false sweetness. "Remember?"

He ran a hand through thinning hair the color of hers. "You'll never let me forget, will you?" He stared at her. "You'll pay me and your mother back for one mistake for the rest of our lives. Just like you're doing now with that outfit, with the coldness in your voice."

"I'd call it more than one mistake, Senator."

"No, only one. Your mother and I should never have divorced, but we also foolishly thought that another divorce for me and whether or not we chose to remarry and all the reasons for and against it were our business and no one else's."

"It became my business when I was forced to realize just where I stood in your life."

He sighed heavily. "So it did," he admitted.

"Why am I here?" Her heart beat heavily as she tried to casually scan the menu. Anything would taste like sawdust right now, so why bother picking and choosing?

"Your mother is in the hospital here. She wants to see you. I want you to visit her."

"You want, she wants. What about what I want?"

"All right, Victoria. What do you want? The last time I tried to talk to you, you didn't seem too clear on the subject. Shall we try again?"

He had stumped her. She didn't know what she wanted. And what was worse, she knew that he knew it, too.

"How's your daughter?" Her voice held an airy quality, a false gaiety.

"She's fine. She's going to have a baby next month."

"Congratulations. You'll be a grandfather." The words stuck in her throat.

He nodded. "For the second time, yes. Your brother's wife had a baby girl three months ago."

"Don't tell me you're claiming it?" Her voice dripped with sarcasm.

"Don't do this to yourself, or to me, Victoria. Keeping alive a hurt that should have died years ago will only make you turn bitter and old before your time."

She gulped past the lump in her throat, angry, yet knowing he was right. But somehow she couldn't stop the words from tumbling out; she couldn't halt the hurt that spilled forth. "I didn't know you cared, Senator. It certainly didn't show before this. What a turnaround! From having one child to claiming two more! My, my, what will the voters think?"

"It's a matter of record that I was married before.

The only person who didn't recognize it was a young girl who accidentally met her half-sister on the street. Was I supposed to shock her or shock you? If it were your decision, which would you have chosen?" The silence was stiff with emotion. It had never been presented to Victoria in that way before, and she was stunned with the choice he had had to make. "Besides, I'm not running again. I'm retiring to live the rest of my days in private. And if your mother pulls through this next ordeal, with God's help, I'll live them with her."

"Leaving your wife?" she sneered.

"My wife left me years ago, Victoria. We live separate lives. She's there for the occasional function when I need her, but she has her friends and I have mine. She'd have no objection if I asked for a divorce. But you didn't know that, did you? If it hadn't been for your mother I would have been a free man by now."

"What did she have to do with it?" Was he trying to softsoap her? No, his expression was too serious, too honest. The word seemed a mockery when connected with him, but it seemed to be the only one that applied.

"Your mother always had a fear of crowds, groups, gatherings. We weren't married a month when we realized just how ill-suited she was for public life. By the time your brother was born we both knew that divorce was the only answer. The problem was that we were still in love with each other and nothing had changed that fact. I convinced myself otherwise and married again, only to find that remarriage wasn't the answer, either. But by that time your mother had decided that she liked the present plan. Before we knew it"—he gave a shrug, his eyes dark with the remembrance of another time—"we were committed to a relationship and a way of life that has lasted all this time. Your mother hated public life and everything it stood for. And it was the only thing I loved, next to her."

"So you had the best of both worlds," she finished bitterly.

"So I walked a tightrope, willing to give neither of them up."

"And will you have enough money to support two families once you retire?"

"I never supported your mother, whatever you may have thought. The house, furniture, daily expenditures, they were all paid for by her with her father's money. She had a good business head on her shoulders, not like your uncle Jake. All I ever gave her was my love." He smiled sadly. "I know it sounds corny to you in today's world, but it's the truth."

Her glistening brown eyes were wide as saucers; the lump in her throat wouldn't go away. In fact, it was growing larger. "Why are you telling me this now? Why didn't you tell me years ago, when I needed to know?"

"Years ago you wouldn't have understood. Everything was black and white to you, with no gray to mess up your personal standards." His eyes grew grave. "But I'm telling you now because I think you'll understand a little more. Maybe not." He shrugged. "I don't know." He gave a small sigh. "It's tough to find out that someone you idolize has feet of clay. As a child you never seemed to see the faults in people until it was too late. Then you hated them for their weaknesses instead of understanding that they were human, just like everyone else. Maybe that hasn't changed."

The waiter took their order, returning a little while later with their food. She was right, the lunch tasted like sawdust, the drink like poison. They spoke little, each eyeing the other furtively. Conflicting thoughts crowded in and out of Victoria's brain. Could there be any truth in what her father had said? She didn't know. She didn't seem to know anything anymore. A few short weeks ago she had thought she had life under control—until she met Kurt. Now it was a mess.

They were sitting over coffee when her father decided to break the silence once more. "Don't make the same mistakes your mother and I did. If you love someone, princess, commit yourself to him. Completely and forever."

"Isn't it a little late for fatherly advice?" She raised an eyebrow, angry that he had read her thoughts. "About seven years too late."

His patience was at an end. He was once more the senator. "Don't be a fool. You can't act the martyr forever. What happened seven years ago can't possibly wipe out the seventeen years before."

She reached for her purse in the chair next to hers. "Goodbye, Senator. Thanks for lunch." Her voice was flippant, her stomach churning over the lunch she hadn't eaten.

"Vicky . . ." He hesitated. "See your mother. For her sake."

"Goodbye."

She spent two days in her townhouse, mulling over the conversation, the inflections of his voice, her reactions, only to wind up back at the same conclusion.

She had to visit her mother.

The night she made that decision, she made another. After drinking three glasses of wine for courage, Victoria picked up the phone and dialed Kurt. He wasn't home. She continued to call every half-hour until the housekeeper was as short-tempered as Vicky was anxious.

At two in the morning she reached him, but not before she had finished several additional glasses of chablis.

"Please come," she whispered brokenly into the phone.

"I'll be right there."

Kurt drove like a maniac toward the townhouse. Vicky had sounded so lonely, so heartbroken, that it had frightened him. He loved her, that was a fact. And if he hadn't been out tonight he would have been with her sooner. His hand hit the steering wheel. Damn! Why had he let Julie talk him into a night on the town for old times' sake? It wasn't because he enjoyed it. There was only one woman who could stir him, and she had been trying to reach him all evening long.

Damn the girl! She was so mixed up that she had begun to mix him up, too! Her fiery, independent streak was going to have to be tamed. She'd have to toe the line and face up to the fact that they belonged together. He suddenly grinned. They'd have a fantastic life together, if they didn't tear each other to pieces first.

Victoria heard his key in the door before she could reach the stairs. She dashed down them, flinging herself into his arms and pressing her head against his sturdy chest.

"You came."

"I came for you," he muttered, suddenly overwhelmed with a need that could not be denied. Reaching down, he swooped her into his arms and marched up the stairs.

Victoria kept her head buried against him, her body singing with unspoken messages of desire. She needed him. How she needed him! He was here, with her, and she didn't have to be alone to face the heartbreak of the past and the fears of the future. Her arms wound around his neck, clutching him tighter.

They reached the bedroom and he put her feet back on the ground, then stood looking down at her, his velvet dark eyes concerned when he saw the tracks of the tears she had cried. His hand came up and undid the clasp that bound her hair, letting it flow around her shoulders. Soon the buttons of her shirt were undone, the material sliding down her soft skin to lie in a small heap on the floor. Her skirt too fell at her feet.

"Come to me now, Victoria. Come to me as a woman who wants her man." His voice shook with emotion, his breath playing along her bare skin as he spoke.

Slowly, but with sure fingers, she undid his tie and shirt, then his slacks, until they both stood naked in the pale golden glow of the small lamp by her bedside.

Her mouth parted silently for his kiss, her arms wrapping around his waist so she could lean against the strength of him. He folded her into his embrace, testing the softness of her slim young body and marveling in the feeling. They blended together, both wanting to be one.

Reluctantly he pulled back to stare hungrily into her eyes as he once more learned the contours of her face. His fingertip followed his gaze, outlining her lips, her brows, her high cheekbones.

"Love me, Kurt," she whispered simply and he complied, giving her no time to change her mind as he laid her on the bed and followed her onto the cushioned softness, his lips silencing anything more she might have said.

Her hands glided over his toughened form, feeling the muscles that moved beneath his skin. He lifted his head to gaze at her once more. Then he lowered it again, taking her mouth roughly this time before moving down her body, savoring her small hollows and slopes, tasting the sweetness of her. Then his mouth returned to hers, fiercely branding her, demanding, his tongue searing her with his heat. His hips pressed closer, telling her without words just how much he needed her, and she responded the same way, showing him that she was ready and willing to be his.

"Here, touch me here," he muttered, taking her

hand and leading it to his chest. "And here." He took it on other travels. "Show me you want me as badly as I want you."

His mouth took her breast, teasing her with the warmth of his tongue. His hand parted the long slim length of her thighs, taunting her with the pleasures to come, and she moaned as the tension built to unbelievable heights.

Then suddenly he was there, and the warmth blazed into a raging heat as lips met and hands caressed and the rhythm of love pulsed between them.

It was a wild, fulfilling ecstasy that made her heart stop beating for eons of time as she arched her back to meet his final thrust. Then came a slow descent that brought her softly back to earth, still in Kurt's enveloping arms.

Kurt's head lay next to hers, his lazy eyes watching the myriad expressions flit across her face. Wonder, love, exhaustion. They were all there.

Her hand ran down the side of his neck, her lips found his throat. "Thank you," she said simply.

He smiled. "You're welcome."

For a moment her eyes closed in contentment, peace flowing through her for the first time since she had spent the weekend with him in Santa Barbara. Was that what she needed? Sex? No, sex could be had with anyone. Only Kurt could give her this sense of completeness and security. Kurt.

He moved and her arms tightened. "Stay," she murmured, and he once again relaxed against her, drawing her back into the comfort of his arms.

She snuggled closer and fell into an immediate, deep sleep.

The early morning sun poured through the window, almost blinding Victoria with its intensity. She reached over to Kurt, only to feel the cold emptiness of the bed. Then she smelled the coffee and she smiled.

Within moments she was dressed and flying down the stairs. She stopped at the bottom, glancing toward the living room, then scanning the kitchen.

"Kurt?" she questioned the emptiness, suddenly afraid again. She could smell his cigarette smoke, but he was nowhere to be seen. He had left, and without him her spirits plummeted.

The door rattled and Kurt walked in, a newspaper in hand. He was dressed in the same slacks, his white shirt open at the collar, *sans* tie. He looked fresh and clean and *solid*. She ran to him.

"Whoa, what's the matter, Victoria?" he asked as she practically knocked him down. His arms went around her, his hands steadying her. One hand slipped under her chin and he stared into her wide eyes. "Did you think I'd gone and hadn't said good-bye?"

She pulled back, suddenly embarrassed. "I didn't know."

"I told you it would be hard to get rid of me. Didn't you believe me? Even after last night?"

Her eyes misted over. "I don't know what to believe anymore. Ever since you've come into my life things have changed." She left the solid comfort of his arms and walked slowly, aimlessly away.

"You can start believing this, Victoria. You're mine. If you never believed it before, last night should have proved it to you. You called me because you needed to be with me as much as I needed you. As soon as we can arrange it, you're marrying me. We'll go from there."

"No! I won't be tied to you. We don't fit the same mold and before long you'd want to leave me for someone else, only you wouldn't, because you'd feel sorry for me, pity me! No!"

He stalked her, grabbing her slim shoulders to keep her near him. "I'm asking you to marry me because that's what I want! Don't you understand that?" His voice softened as he saw the velvet moistness in her wide, frightened eyes. "I want to wake up every morning and find you there. I want to share the day's events with you, watch you grow big with my children, laugh and cry with you." His voice dropped an octave. "I love you."

Suddenly she was frightened again. Not of him, but of the total commitment he was asking her for. "And what happens to your lovely mistress? Will you still be taking her out on the town? Escorting her all over the hot spots of Los Angeles? Am I supposed to wait at home like a good wife and hope that you'll come home to me after leaving her bed?"

His face turned white at her accusation, his fingers tightening their hold on her shoulders. The dark smudge of her lashes hid her thoughts from him, making him angrier than ever.

"There will be no one else for either of us, Vicky. Ever."

And somehow she knew he was right. But even so, a deep-seated fear of the commitment he was demanding ate at her soul. How could she be sure? How?

He spent the night with her again, his anger curbed enough to allow him to hold her, touch her.

Victoria was frightened. Her skin tightened as if an adversary were near and she would be called upon to fight to the death. Her eyes continued to probe the corners of the room. She waited expectantly for something disastrous to happen and the waiting scraped her nerves raw.

Her restlessness must have kept him awake, for he finally heaved a deep sigh and gathered her into his arms, stroking her back as if she were a baby. The motion was soothing and she finally drifted into sleep.

In the middle of the night she reached out to find the warmth of Kurt's body, but he was gone and sleep fled. It took her a little time to adjust to the darkness, but when she did she saw him silhouetted against the bright, moonlit window. He was leaning against the frame, a glowing cigarette cupped in his hand. The moonglow showed the serious, contemplative expression on his face, etching it with brilliant white and jagged black shadows. She was afraid to move for fear of interrupting him, intruding when he wanted to be alone, so she watched. He looked so lonely, so separate from the rest of the world. Her heart went out to him, hurting with her own need to comfort—and be comforted.

He took a drag of his cigarette and a shiver suddenly ran down her spine at the power he exuded. He had the look of a barbarian: raw, naked, powerful, in his own right. A survivor. He was a contradiction of everything she had ever believed the man she would love to be. He was bossy and arrogant, yet tender and gentle, leading her down paths she had never traveled before. He could whip her with words at a second's notice, yet his kisses were passionate and giving, tender and loving.

And he loved her.

He stubbed out the cigarette in the ashtray on the windowsill, then returned to comtemplating the illuminated scenery, pondering a problem of which she had no knowledge. His broad chest moved slowly with his steady breathing.

"Kurt?" she finally whispered from the dark. "Come back to me."

He turned slowly, his face still serious. She sat up and clutched the sheet to her breasts, her whole body a question. Did he hate her? Had she destroyed all that he had given her with her thoughtless words of the morning? Was he disgusted with her?

Kurt walked to the bed and slipped beneath the light covers, turning to hold her close to his cool skin. He stroked her arm as he lay back with a sigh. "Rest, darling," he muttered into her hair, his deep voice rumbling in her ear.

"I'm sorry about what I said." Her voice was small, weak—and she hated herself for the weakness—but the words had to be said. "I just needed to lash out at someone, and you were there."

"I know and I understand." His hand lightly cupped her breast. "But that doesn't mean I forgive you."

"What *does* it mean, then?" Her voice had hardened. Only two minutes ago she had been looking at him as if she were the only friend he had in the world, and now she felt as if she were ready to feed him to the lions!

"It means that you're responsible for your actions, and childish temper tantrums are not acceptable at your age." He slid further under the covers, his head tilting toward hers.

But her compassion for him had fled. "I don't have tantrums." Her voice was stiff with anger. "You're just an impossible person to reason with and I lose my temper with you, that's all."

"Victoria?" His voice sounded so tired, so weary, and her heart softened.

"Yes?" she whispered softly.

"Shut up and go to sleep. I'm not going to argue with you. Especially when *I* know that *you* know I'm right," he muttered. "We'll finish this in the morning. Then you can call me all sorts of names and I can receive them in the spirit in which they're intended. Goodnight."

"Go to hell."

A low vibration closely resembling a chuckle rattled against her ear. "Not when I'm holding heaven in my arms, sweet Victoria." He gave her a soft squeeze, ignoring her stiffened body, and fell promptly to sleep.

It took her a long time to let go of her anger enough to relax. But finally she did, with a small smile on her lips as she remembered the gruffness of his tone as he spoke to her and his firm but tender hold on her breast as he held her. He obviously wasn't angry enough to allow her to sleep alone. . . .

The hospital corridors were painted a sterile off-white. Wide and well-lit, they reminded Victoria of a prison she had once written a small piece on. No matter what the decor, you could never hide the fact that a hospital was a hospital. Her steps were measured, moving her forward even when she didn't want to go. Room 404.

Her mother's hair, once as dark as her own, was streaked with gray. Her face had aged; there were small wrinkles around her eyes and chin. There was a deep, haunting quality, vulnerable and yet hopeful, about the tentative smile she gave to Victoria.

"You came. I'm glad; I missed you," the older woman said, although speaking was an obvious drain on her strength.

Victoria's heart twisted in her breast. How could she have torn her mother apart like this? Hadn't seven years taught her how to be an adult?

"Of course I came. I've missed you, Mom." She took her mother's hand in hers, her lips grazing the older woman's cheek.

"Your father told me he had lunch with you. He said he tried to explain things to you." She gave a small smile, a faint twinkle in her eyes. "But he said you took after me and had mentally run away from him again even before the discussion was over."

"I don't know what you mean."

"Oh, yes, you do, my dear. And I know what your

father means. I used to run away all the time myself."

Victoria's eyes widened. "You did? When?"

"I tried to run away from your father. Oh, don't give me that look, Victoria—it usually means you're closing yourself off from whatever you don't want to hear. But I don't know how much time I have left, so I'm going to say my piece. This illness has made me realize I'm not as immortal as I thought." Her mother smiled as she spoke and Victoria couldn't help but smile in return.

"All right, Mother. I'll listen."

Her mother's hand stroked back Victoria's long dark hair, her eyes dimming as she reached into the past and saw the Victoria that used to be as a child. "I named you Victoria because I hoped that you would have Victorian manners, be reticent, charming and demure, with none of the wild, wicked ways of your mother. But it didn't work out that way. You were always getting into things, challenging my authority, seeking answers to questions that I thought time would answer for you if you were patient enough." She chuckled softly. "But you were too much like me; even your father saw that."

"When he was around." Victoria tried to keep the bitterness out of her voice, but apparently she didn't succeed.

"He was almost always around in your youth, Victoria. He tried to be there for you. He loved you very much, and no matter how hard you try, you can't deny that, even if he didn't always know how to express his love." Her mother's voice was firm with conviction. "He never got a divorce to remarry me because I never wanted him to. I wanted both worlds, my very private life *and* your father. I didn't stop to weigh circumstances or consider the feelings of others. I did what I wanted." She sighed heavily. "And I was wrong."

Victoria continued to hold her mother's fragile hand, not knowing what to say and not wanting to think of her mother's words. They hit too close to home.

"I thought I was a free spirit, no ties, no lasting commitments, because those would demand something from me in return. I didn't see that by my own selfishness I was tying your father to a life that he wasn't allowed to take pride in. I thought that was his problem, not mine."

"He could have said no at any time, Mother."

"No, he couldn't. By the time he realized what had happened to us he was too in love to reason out a sensible answer. Love does strange things, dear. It makes you do things you would never dream of doing otherwise, say things that hurt when you want to soothe, dream of a way of life that just isn't realistic. I did that to your father, and to you and your brother. And all so I could have my freedom."

"And do you?"

"No. You can't have both freedom and a real, lasting love." Visibly tired, she leaned her head back against the pillow and stared at the ceiling for a few moments, her hand tightening in Victoria's every so often. The room was filled with a poignant silence. Tears formed and rolled down Victoria's cheeks at the sadness of it all. "And never to love is too high a price to pay for freedom, Victoria. Much too high."

Victoria wiped the tears from her eyes and stepped out into the sterile hallway a little while later. She sniffed, then looked up to stare at the two men she had not wanted to see: her father and Kurt. They stood just a few feet away, deep in conversation. She could sense the tone of what they were saying, but couldn't hear the words. Kurt nodded his head, his eyes on the floor as he listened intently to whatever her father was saying.

"Am I interrupting something?" Her voice was cold, more in self-defense than because she was angry.

Both men's eyes hooded over. Her father, an expert politician, put on his best campaign face and smiled. "Nothing important, Victoria." He turned sober eyes on her. "Will you visit your mother again?"

"Yes, of course," she said softly, placing her hand on his arm in reassurance. For once she forgot the animosity between them as she saw the sadness and pain in his eyes. "I'll be back tomorrow."

"Good." He bent down and gave her cheek a peck, then turned quickly to shake hands with Kurt, as if embarrassed and not wanting to chance a rebuke from his daughter. "I'll see you again sometime, Kurt. Take care."

Victoria watched him march stiffly down the hall and into her mother's room. Her emotions had run the gamut in the past few days and suddenly she was exhausted. Kurt must have sensed it, because he took her arm and led her out of the hospital and toward his car, placing her in the passenger seat without uttering a word, then headed toward her apartment.

It had been years since Victoria had sat face to face with her mother and listened to her voice. And now that she had seen her mother again all the confusion and childish emotions she thought she had put behind her came crashing back like boulders falling into the sea. Memories of being inside the lovingness of her family, being encased in their comfort and caring arms, swirled around her.

And when she returned to her apartment, and Kurt left, she would be totally alone. Again. Only this time, she vowed, if it happened, it wouldn't be by choice.

She sat straight up in her seat, her eyes suddenly bright. "Kurt, take me to Hal's for a hot dog; please?"

He glanced at her before staring back out at the traffic ahead. "Aren't you tired, Victoria? Wouldn't you rather let me take you home and fix you something to eat there?"

"No." She shook her head. "Home is too . . . too. . . ." She was going to say too filled with solitude, but his next words interrupted her train of thought.

"Too intimate? Are you afraid I might want to make love to you again? Is that it, Victoria?"

"No! That isn't what I meant at all."

"Then what did you mean? It's obvious that you don't want to be alone with me. Give me another reason for not wanting to go home."

"It's just too lonely, that's all," she mumbled stiffly.

He gave an exasperated sigh, his hands tightening on the wheel. "Even with me there, you're lonely?"

"No, but when you leave, then. . . ." She couldn't

complete the thought. A shudder passed through her and she realized just how close she was to tears.

Kurt turned off the freeway and drove toward Hal's, his face shuttered.

They sat in a corner booth, munching on hot dogs they didn't really want and discussing topics they didn't care about. Neither was willing to broach the one subject closest to them: their feelings for each other.

Finally Kurt stood, throwing down his napkin and reaching out a hand. "Let's go." His eyes sent her a message and she responded by giving his hand a light squeeze before following him out the door and to the car.

When they reached her townhouse the tension stretched between them. Victoria busied herself with making coffee he hadn't asked for, her hands trembling slightly. When she returned to the living room Kurt was sitting on the couch, his hands behind his head as he stared at the loft above.

"I've been here many times, but never has that small loft intrigued me as it has since you've been here," he mused, almost to himself. His eyes locked with hers, refusing to allow her to pretend she didn't know what he wanted. "When will you give yourself— all of yourself—to me willingly?" he wondered aloud.

She held out her hand to him. She was no longer lonely, but basking in the love that suddenly shone from his eyes. "Now," she promised softly.

# 8

They made love slowly, leisurely, as if they had captured and held all the time in the world. They touched, tasted one another, gave their love freely and without reservation, knowing that neither had ever known such an intense feeling before.

They lay in each other's arms, frightened of losing the closeness they had just gained. Kurt's arms surrounded her protectively, the palm of his hand gently soothing the small hollow at the base of her spine. She nestled against his chest, the top of her head just under his chin.

"Don't stop," she mumbled and his chest rose with a deep, vibrating chuckle.

"Yes, ma'am. At your service, ma'am."

She answered his teasing with a light jab in the ribs that turned out to be more of a caress.

"Am I doing it wrong, ma'am? Am I too rough? Am I too gentle? Just tell me what to do and how to do it. I'll try anything to keep you happy, ma'am." His tone was teasing, but when she looked into his eyes she knew that a portion of him was totally serious. And suddenly she was frightened.

"Kurt, I . . ."

He placed a finger lightly over her mouth, silencing her. "Shhh, Victoria. Don't spoil it now."

Her eyes showed the anguish that had just surfaced, breaking through the temporary euphoria in her mind, the total indecision and frustration of feeling like a floundering piece of seaweed with no roots, no home. But as afraid as she was of that homeless feeling, she was also afraid of finding roots, only to have them taken away from her when the newness wore off and the sameness of their routine made Kurt look elsewhere. Did he understand? Could he understand? She didn't know.

She burrowed back against the hardness of his chest, her bottom lip tucked behind her teeth to keep the words from spilling out and making an even bigger fool of herself. Her hand caressed his midriff, feeling the tautness of his bronzed skin. Perhaps this was the home she was seeking. Perhaps home wasn't a place to be, but a person to be with. Perhaps . . .

Kurt heaved a heavy, tired sigh as if her weight was too much for him to handle, and she moved slightly, giving him more breathing space. "I've got to go. I have calls that have to be returned today, things to take care of. When you told me that you were visiting your mother, I left my office immediately without telling my secretary where I was going."

"Oh, by all means. Business before pleasure." She was hurt by his words.

"Don't be a child, Victoria. We both have jobs to do. You've told me so yourself. And because I didn't want you to see your parents by yourself, I've been neglecting my work."

"I'm sorry," she said stiffly, getting up and walking proudly to the closet to take out a robe. When she had wrapped it firmly around her body she turned to face Kurt, who still lay on the bed, watching her with a speculative gleam in his narrowed eyes.

"Meet me for dinner tonight."

"We'll see."

"Don't play coy; it doesn't become you."

"Then what does? Lying naked in bed all day? Pleasing you? What?"

The late afternoon sun suddenly disappeared behind a dark cloud, leaving the room cold. Kurt stood and reached for his pants, stepping into them quickly, with an effortless motion. Within a minute he was dressed, facing her, challenging her with a look. "I'll send the car for you at eight. Be ready."

It was an order, one that she knew she would obey.

The dress was simple and understated. Victoria turned this way and that, trying to decide whether it was too simple. Kurt hadn't explained his plans for the evening, so this would have to do. When the bell rang she reached for her purse and opened the door to his overly polite driver. It was going to be a long evening if Kurt was half as stiff as his hired help. This man could shrivel a grape into a raisin, and all without the help of mother nature!

"Where are we going?" she asked, more to hear a voice than because she was interested in her destination. As long as Kurt was there. . . .

"You and Mr. Morgan are attending a private dinner party this evening at the home of Mr. James Borman, the head of the International Exchange for our state. Mr. Morgan is waiting for you there."

"Oh, my," she murmured, "I do believe I've been outclassed."

The moment she stepped into the house she wondered why she had come. The living room was decorated with dark, impressive antiques. The men were grouped around the fireplace drinking, while the women sat chatting in small conversational groups. The moment Kurt saw her he broke away and walked toward her, his hand outstretched, a glimmer of relief in his eyes.

"I'm glad you came," he muttered.

"I feel as if I've just been transported back in time . . . to my first dance," she returned, smiling with relief herself.

He took her arm and began leading her through the long room toward their host, who was standing near the fireplace.

"Your first dance? Why?"

"Because that was the last time I saw the boys lined up on one side with girls on the other."

His head went back as he gave a hearty laugh, startling the other guests and bringing a smile to his host's face. "Jim, I'd like you to meet a most delightful guest. Victoria, Jim."

They shook hands, with Jim's kind pale gray eyes

staring down into hers. "I'm glad to meet anyone, Victoria, who can make this stodgy man laugh."

"Thank you." She was suddenly shy. One of the uniformed waiters handed her a crystal glass of champagne. She glanced sideways at Kurt, who was still grinning broadly. "It isn't easy."

She stood with Kurt for a few moments before excusing herself to find the rest room, more for a lack of anything else to do than from necessity.

She sat at a makeup table, playing with the contents of her purse as she watched the other women pass in and out of the small room attached to the dressing room. Most of the women were in their forties or older, well-preserved, fashionable, expertly made-up. All but one or two wore an expression of contentment. Did that mean they were satisfied with their way of life, or with their marriages or both? she wondered. Were late and weekend business meetings something that went with the territory, merely the drawbacks of the business of making money? Had these women ever loved as she loved Kurt? Did they get dizzy from the nearness of their husbands, taste the sweetness of their lips and have to beg for more? A small grin creased Victoria's cheeks. Somehow she couldn't imagine these women going week-kneed from across a crowded room.

She reluctantly rejoined the gathering, accepting another glass of courage from a wandering waiter. Sipping without tasting, she scanned the small scattered groups until she found Kurt. He was watching her with as much intensity as she had displayed while trying to locate him. One of the men standing beside him gave him a nudge in the ribs, whispering something that made him glance over his shoulder before grinning at the nudger, then walk toward Victoria. His eyes never left her, pleasure plainly written on his face.

"I thought you'd never get back. How much can you do to a face that's already so perfect?"

"I didn't do anything. I just sat and listened to some of the other women discuss their lives, their neighbors and the care and feeding of the American husband." Her eyes twinkled, not so much from the small joke but because she was with Kurt again . . . and that made her unbearably happy.

"Ready to go?" He took her arm and began leading her into the hall.

"We can't go now! Kurt, be reasonable! What will our host say? After all, this is supposed to include dinner."

He stopped in the center of the foyer, his hands tightening on her arms. Warm waves of heat engulfed her.

"I can't think straight. Every time I look across at you I want to carry you off to bed somewhere, anywhere, where I can hold you and make love to you all night." He took her hand and placed it just inside his jacket. "Feel my heartbeat. You do that to me. You turn me into a geiger counter, ticking away."

"Hey, folks!" their host exclaimed from the entrance of the dining room. "It's time to join the rest of us and have dinner."

Kurt took her arm and reluctantly steered her to a seat directly across from him. The table was long and narrow, easily seating the twenty guests without crowding. It was set with the finest of ecru linen and silver, with small crystal bowls of floating candles and gardenias strategically placed along the length of the table.

Victoria watched Kurt move around to the other side, every step making his tuxedo hug the muscles of his back and arms. A deep-seated yearning to be held by him arched through her body. It wasn't so much his physical embrace she craved as the simple nearness of him. She needed his strength, his wisdom, his comfort. Suddenly she felt terribly sad. Was it because she was denying herself the lifelong pleasure of him by not accepting his proposal? Had she become so confused by her parents' relationship that it stunted her potential to be a loving, caring being? She hadn't thought so until now. But, looking back, she had always shunned the dates who might have been interested in her as a person in favor of those who just wanted to have fun. That fact was a revelation to Victoria. She had never delved into that portion of her psyche before, and what she was finding now didn't make her feel comfortable at all. Always afraid of deepening relationships, she had managed to keep at bay anyone who could have truly cared for her.

A shoe softly tapped her foot and she glanced up, startled, to look into Kurt's deep brown eyes. He raised one dark brow in a silent question and she smiled back, keeping none of her most intimate feelings from shining in her eyes, warming him with her glance.

His breath shook in his lungs as he watched her smile break like the slow-moving surf at dawn, glistening with newness and the promise of things to come. Slowly raising his long-stemmed wine glass, he saluted her with an unspoken answer to her silent invitation. It was a pledge to both of them.

The conversation drifted around the table, talk of business, money market trends, politics. Dinner was served in stately elegance by two women in short black uniforms. Victoria was hard-pressed not to laugh at the predictability of it. It was so much like a movie would be!

She glanced at Kurt, only to find him staring at her, and her eyes once more dropped to her plate. Her earlier mood had disappeared, to be replaced by a carefree feeling. It didn't matter that they had to appear sedate and dignified right now. They both knew that when they reached home they could giggle, laugh, touch . . . love.

A small impish grin lifted up the corners of her mouth as the germ of an idea was born. Kurt looked so serious, so dignified as he answered a question the woman on his left had asked. Victoria managed to slip off her high-heeled sandal. Continuing to eat daintily, she straightened her stockinged leg until it met Kurt's. He glanced up, startled, but she demurely continued with her meal as her toes crept underneath his pants leg, dancing lightly across the grain of his dark silk sock.

"Don't you find that so, Miss Brown?" the older woman at Kurt's side questioned.

Victoria's fork clattered to her plate. "I beg your pardon?"

"Don't you find you feel better without air conditioning?"

"I'm afraid I enjoy the heat, so my opinion of air conditioning would be biased to begin with," she said with a polite smile as her foot continued on its light-as-air path up and down Kurt's calf. He looked positively rigid, as if turned into stone. "What do you think, Kurt? How do you feel about air conditioning?"

His smile was stiff, but his voice was calm enough. "I believe I could use a little right now."

Her eyes widened in innocence. "Oh, really? And I thought it was comfortable in here."

"So did I," the older woman murmured, glancing at Kurt as if he had something catching. "Are you feeling well, Mr. Morgan?"

"It's nothing serious. I'm sure that in a few hours I'll be as good as new," he said blandly, his eyes sending Victoria a silent message. She had a feeling that she knew what it was that would make him feel better. The thing was, she wasn't sure if he wanted to beat her or make love to her, or both!

Dessert was served just as the conversation slowly dwindled to a standstill, thank goodness. The chocolate mousse was perfect, the taste and texture exquisite. Victoria's foot finally halted its sensuous pilgrimage so she could pay attention to her dessert. Suddenly Kurt kicked her ankle lightly and she jumped. His dark eyes held her captive and a deep sweet yearning built in the depths of her stomach until it was an almost tangible, living pain. He was everything to her. She forgot that they were sitting at a table with eighteen people. She forgot everything except for her total need of the man across from her. She was lost in a bemused daze.

"Is something bothering you, Victoria?" her host questioned, his brow furrowed. "You look as if you're concentrating on something."

A slow flush worked its way up her slim neck and into her cheeks.

"Perhaps Miss Brown is worried about something," Kurt interjected. "Did you forget to turn something off at your apartment?"

"Of course not!" she denied emphatically before she realized she had been given a perfect way out of the rest of the evening. "Well, perhaps," she said in a softer tone. "I can't remember." Good grief! That was stupid! "I mean, yes, I did leave something on and I think I'd better check on it immediately."

"Of course. Shall I have the phone brought in here so you can call a neighbor?" Jim Borman asked.

"Oh, no. I mean. . . ." Victoria looked helplessly from Kurt to her host and back again. The entire table was now quiet, listening to the conversation, curiosity plainly written on their usually carefully controlled faces.

"I believe Victoria would like to check her apartment personally. You see, she just moved into a new townhouse and doesn't know any of her neighbors yet."

"Oh, I understand," Jim sympathized, standing. "I hope it's not too far away for you or you'll probably worry all the way there."

Kurt rose, but Victoria continued to sit, her face flushed, one stockinged foot frantically searching for her shoe.

"Are you ready, Victoria? If so, I'll take you home." Kurt waited for her to respond before a wide, knowing grin split his face.

Victoria was becoming angrier by the minute. He looked as if he would love to burst out laughing and only propriety held it in!

Finally she found her shoe and slipped into it, then rose. "Thank you for a delicious dinner. It's been a pleasure to meet you." She walked regally from the room, her hand resting on Kurt's arm.

As they passed the end of the table one of the women leaned over and muttered *sotto voce* to her companion, "I wonder if he put her in the same townhouse that he had his last girlfriend in. Very convenient for him."

"And you'd give your eyeteeth to know the gory details, wouldn't you, Alice?" the man answered in a tired voice.

The warm night air fanned Victoria's cheeks but didn't seem to help her building temper at all. So he had put her in his last girlfriend's apartment, had he? So he had professed his love only to treat her the same as all the others, had he? It didn't matter that she had just realized how foolish she had been in turning down his proposal. For all she knew he could have tried that tactic with every woman interested in him. Damn him! And she had been ready to fall right in with his plans as if she had thought them up herself! What a fool she was!

"I know what you're thinking, Vicky; I heard that woman, too. But don't jump to conclusions." Kurt walked her calmly to his car, his voice even. "I'm tired of your mood swings. I want you to listen to me. From now on you'll do what's good for you."

"And you're the only one who knows what that is, I suppose?" She had to be sarcastic or she would burst into tears.

"Yes." He slammed the car into gear, almost tearing down the drive and around the corner. "Now behave yourself until we get home or I'll pull off to the side of the road and we can have it out here."

His tone was enough to keep her quiet. But the closer they got to the apartment, the whiter Kurt's knuckles became and the calmer Victoria felt. It was funny, but she knew that although he had put her into his mistress' old apartment Kurt didn't really think of her that way. He had been too persistent, too loving, to have treated her as just another woman among many. She loved him with all her heart, but her own unsure emotions kept getting in the way, not allowing her to tell him of her own commitment to him. She kept clouding the issue with excuses, fears carried over from her past, not based on a realistic picture of the present—or the future. And that wasn't fair to either of them—not if they were to make a life together.

By the time they reached her apartment Victoria had been properly chastised by her own conscience. By the time they reached her door she was more than ready to confess her sins and ask him to marry her. But when he turned around to put the safety lock on, then turned on all the lights before standing in the center of the living room to stare at her as if she were the last person he wished to see, she lost the nerve to say anything!

"Kurt . . . ?" She sounded as hesitant as she felt. How could she explain?

"Don't say another word, Victoria," he gritted between clenched teeth. "I'll be damned if I can figure you out. What do you want from me? You won't be my wife, so whose fault is it if people think you're my mistress?" He walked to the window, then turned, his hands clenched in his pockets, to face her once more. "When I met you I fell instantly in love, despite your silly disguise. You seemed to be innocent, sensuous, understanding, intelligent. Everything I had ever wanted, and I could hardly believe my luck. I honestly believed that every barrier you built I'd be able to tear down. I thought you were frightened of a deep relationship and tried to go gently. What a big mistake in judgment I made. Now I see that you're just like any other woman, selfish, wanting everything and giving nothing."

"Yes, I'm selfish! I want to think that the man I'm with is one hundred percent with me, too! How do you think I feel knowing that your previous mistress used to occupy these premises? Am I supposed to be thankful she's not here now?" She took a deep breath before continuing, her anger turning into a full-force gale. To think that *she* had been ready to apologize!

Well, not anymore. "Let the big ox have it" would be her motto from now on!

"You're no different from any other man! Just because you have money you think you can snap your fingers and everyone will kowtow to your every whim! Well, not this girl! This girl is moving out next week and letting someone else have this romantic little hideaway! So you'd better start looking for a replacement!"

She stared wide-eyed at him, a hand to her mouth as she realized what she had just said. A terrible feeling of fear cloaked her, suddenly making her see that the path she had just set herself upon—a life without Kurt—was unbearable. She didn't mean it; she would make him see that she didn't.

Victoria took a step toward him, her hand out in supplication. "Kurt, I . . ."

His face was expressionless, his voice stiff. "Don't say any more, Victoria. I think you've said enough for both of us. And now I think I'll leave." He walked to the door. "Somehow I knew that everything I thought I saw in you was just a pipe dream. I've never kidded myself before. It's a shame I did it this time." He hesitated for only a moment. "Goodbye, Victoria Branden Brown."

His tone was as final as the slam of the door.

"How long have you been a male stripper, Chet?" Victoria questioned without curiosity. She was interviewing a young man who danced at one of the Los Angeles nightclubs where only women were allowed in the audience. The only men were the dancers and waiters, and women flocked to sit and squander dollar bills on their favorites.

Chet was one of those dancers. After sending query letters to several magazines and newspapers, Victoria had received enough interest in an article on the phenomenon to set up an interview with him. Last week it had seemed like an interesting story to write. Today it was boring. All Victoria really wanted to do was sit in a darkened room and cry out her misery. It had been two days and Kurt hadn't called or come by. Obviously he didn't want to see her again. . . .

"I've been on the stage for about three years now," he answered, popping his gum and looking as bored as she felt. "I started because I needed the money for college and it paid well."

"You have a college degree?" Her voice rose an octave. She hadn't counted on this bit of information.

He grinned, pleased that he had surprised her, and his boyish dimples creased his handsome face. He was really beautiful to look at, with a magnificent body and a very disarming personality when he decided to turn on the charm. She had seen him do so to an older woman in the bar the night she set up this interview. The woman had practically melted in her seat, promptly paying him ten dollars for the favor of his kiss.

"I have a degree in Secondary Education. I'm ready to teach history to little junior high school students . . . as soon as I've finished having my fun dancing for my supper."

"What kind of schedule do you maintain to stay in

shape?" His build was flawless. He looked as if he were in training for body building, as did all the dancers.

"I pump iron, that's lift weights, three times a week in a gym near my apartment. Other than that, I can pretty much do what I want or eat what I want. Dancing three nights out of seven means I can lose at least five or ten pounds a week." Again he grinned disarmingly. He sensed her interest and began to pour on the charm. After all, her apartment was expensive and although she was young, you never knew. . . .

Victoria could almost see the thoughts cross his face and a sudden pang of loneliness seared through her. Where was Kurt and what was he doing right now? Was he taking a beautiful actress to lunch? Was he flirting with someone over a glass of chilled wine, wondering if she would be warm and soft in bed? Was he missing her half as much as she pined for him?

"Say," Chet exclaimed, pushing himself out of his seat and toward her, "are you all right?"

The concern in his voice brought a film of tears to her eyes and she blinked rapidly. "I'm sorry. Dust got in my eyes," Victoria lied, wiping her lids with the backside of her hand and giving a curious, sad smile. "Go on with what you were saying."

Chet leaned back on his heels, his eyes searching her face for the answer to her sudden tears. But he found none. Instead he realized just how lovely the young girl in front of him was. She was clear-skinned, with beautiful big brown eyes and long dark hair that reached all the way down her back. Maybe she didn't have much going financially, but she was a knockout!

"You know, you're really pretty."

Victoria gave a watery chuckle. "So are you."

A teasing light shone in his bright blue eyes. "I know. I'd better be; it's my stock and trade."

"Oh, but you have teaching to fall back on," she quipped, attempting to match his lighthearted mood.

"And even though you're beautiful, you have your writing to fall back on," he reminded her with just a touch of seriousness. "And now it's my turn to ask the questions. What made you decide to earn a living this way? Isn't it a little unusual? After all, you could have been a secretary."

"Writing was always my first love. Ever since I can remember I've wanted to write."

"And now you do."

She agreed. "And now I do."

"And is it as great as you thought it would be? Are there any flaws that you see up close that you weren't able to see before?"

"Lots." A vision of Kurt flashed before her eyes. She would never have met him if it hadn't been for her writing. And now, with her writing, she would attempt to fill the enormous void that he had made by leaving her to face the rest of her life alone. Her eyes saw far into the future. "Without it I would be lost."

"But not for all the right reasons, I suspect," Chet muttered, still concerned. He had come here to do an interview and see what would come of it, imagining what a kick it would be to see his picture and name in print, wondering if some big-time producer would ask him to star in a film. Now, here he was, suddenly worried about the interviewer! "I think I smell a love affair gone sour."

"So much for good-looking noses."

"The nose knows," Chet persisted. "Was he mean and nasty? Did he leave you for another woman? Did he ignore you and leave a mess in his wake? Any of the above?"

She couldn't help but chuckle. If she didn't she just might cry, and that wouldn't do. "No, to all of the above. I was a fool and he was a perfect gentleman."

"Then he should be here now."

"He got tired of my temper tantrums and left." There, she had finally admitted it to herself. That was exactly what had happened. Again a pain seared through her. The loss was so great. . . .

"Listen, lady. I don't know how they do things here, but in my territory, if you want someone you go after him."

Victoria couldn't smile. Her eyes had a hurt, glazed look. "If I did that in my territory, he'd turn his back on me."

Chet's brows rose. "Why? Men love being chased, too. I bet he's praying for you to make a move right now. If he's half as wonderful as you think he is, he should be miserable and just waiting for you to beg him to come back," he reasoned. "Trust me, I'm a whiz at things like this. I've got a kind of second sight when it comes to people. And I'd bet a night's tips on this one." Chet leaned back, his look deceptively casual. "That is, if he's what you really want. Maybe he's not worth it after all."

Victoria's mind whirled with this new possibility. Kurt had always had to make the initial moves, circumvent her arguments and put up with her temper tantrums. Could he just be biding his time to see how much she cared? Could he . . . ?

"Do you think so?"

"Sure." Chet mentally crossed his fingers. This was one miserable lady and his idea was at least worth a try. "And if he isn't, then give me a call and we'll do the town together. I know a classy lady when I see one."

Chet stood and held out his hand, smiling down at her tear-streaked face as he silently cursed himself for falling for a woman's tears. He'd never been able to withstand them, even as a kid. "Tell you what. Take your chances with the guy and go after him. If it works you owe me the biggest and best story you can write, promoting me as the next Valentino." He winked. "Deal?"

"Deal," she finally said, her hand slipping into his. "And whether you're right or wrong, I'll write that story," she promised, giving him her first real smile.

It took two glasses of wine and three hours for Victoria to realize just what a coward she was. She had always had a temper, but over the past few years she had thought she had learned how to control it. But with Kurt she had proven she couldn't, time and time again. And now she couldn't even apologize properly for her own lack of control.

It was because of her that they had gone from the expectation of ecstasy to breaking up so completely so quickly. Why hadn't she had the sense to keep her mouth shut? Was she so self-destructive that she had to wreck whatever happiness came her way?

Was there a flaw in her character that wouldn't allow her to see what she wanted until it was too late to do anything about it? Apparently so. For so many years she had accused her parents of wrecking her happy home, but it had always been just the same. It was only the fact that she knew more about her parents' relationship that had made it different. The hard truth was that they hadn't changed, she had. And she had thought she had known everything. How sanctimonious teenagers could be!

And now, looking back, she realized that she had carried her juvenile emotions into an adult man to woman relationship that meant more than the world to her. She had acted and reacted like a child. No wonder she had lost him.

Then the solution came to her. A small smile played around her mouth as she envisioned the scene that would begin in Kurt's office. It had to work. It would work!

# 9

~~~~~~~~~~~~~~~

The Newstime Tower stood silhouetted against the dusty pale blue of the Los Angeles skyline. Victoria strode straight to the front door. She looked totally chic and very much a part of the scene, wearing a sleek black dress with a high collar, short capped sleeves and a slit up one side to expose a barely decent length of tan leg; her long dark brown hair piled in a loose but very attractive knot on the top of her head and fastened with large wooden pins.

She walked straight into an elevator and rose quickly to the executive suite. But as Victoria walked down the long carpeted hallway toward Kurt's office her spirit began to falter. What if he wouldn't see her? What if he wouldn't accept her? What if he didn't want to have anything to do with her, ever again? What if he really thought that she was just too juvenile for him? What if he wasn't willing to take the time to show her the right way to grow, to learn, to satisfy? She gave a deep sigh. And all this was because it had taken her seven years longer to grow up than it should have!

She hesitated just outside the glass door that led to the reception area of his office and peered in, seeing his secretary talking on the phone as she scratched something on a memo pad. Victoria's hands were clammy with perspiration, her nerves stretched tight. Her eyes darted about the area, unconsciously seeking a place to hide if necessary. What would she do if she couldn't get past Kurt's watchdog?

She straightened her shoulders. It was the rest of her life that was at stake. She'd get past his secretary if it killed her! She had to!

Victoria gave the woman her best smile, looking what she hoped was confident and self-assured. "I'd like to see Mr. Morgan, please."

"Do you have an appointment?" Margie took in the appearance of the girl in front of her. She seemed to be sweet, but there was a definite sense of panic in the air.

"I didn't think I needed one." She forced a light, airy laugh, only she sounded like a croaking frog to her own ears. "After all, I am his intended." His intended! Couldn't she have said something, anything, except that? That sounded like it came straight out of a period romance or something! "I mean, we're engaged. We're getting married."

"I see," Margie muttered dryly. "And does the bridegroom know about this? Or are you here to inform him of the fact now?"

Victoria flushed a deep red. Just then Kurt's office door opened and he ushered an older man out, his eyes turning to chipped ice when he spied Victoria.

She smiled brightly, but it wasn't returned. He was surprised to see her, but he certainly didn't look happy.

She walked toward him, her arms out as if to embrace the world. "Darling!" Her voice was supposed to sound throaty; instead it sounded hoarse.

"Your, uh, intended just announced herself to me, Mr. Morgan. I haven't had a chance to announce her to you." Margie left the one big question hanging in the air. Was he really engaged?

"My intended?" Kurt's attitude became even chillier, if that was possible. He held her arms away from him, staring down at her face. "That's because she's not my 'intended,' Margie." Victoria's heart dropped to her knees. "She has a great deal of explaining to do and then she has to propose, properly, on one knee. And then, I'll make my decision." His voice was as grim as a death knell, but his words put a giggle in Victoria's heart. He would listen to her! He would!

She followed him into his office, her head bowed contritely until the outer door was shut and they were alone.

Peeping through her lashes she saw him cross his arms and take a waiting stance. His brows were still etched in a dark, ominous frown. She took a deep breath.

"Will you marry me, Kurt Morgan?" she questioned testily. After all, she wasn't totally at fault here. He *had* had another mistress before her, and he had kept her in the same apartment! She forgot that this same topic was the very thing that had torn them apart a few days before.

"I don't think so, but thanks anyway," he said calmly.

Her eyes opened wide. After that speech to his secretary she hadn't expected him to say no! "What?"

"I said no, thank you." His dark brown eyes glanced off her and stared out the window as if he were bored with the whole conversation. "Now, if there's nothing else . . . ?"

"Who in the hell do you think you are? I came here in good faith, ready to apologize for all the bad times I've put you through! The least you can do is listen to what I have to say!" she shouted, hands on hips.

Kurt walked slowly to the window and continued to stare out, his back toward her. "All right, say what you have to say. I have other things to do today."

Victoria's thoughts raced so wildly in her brain that she couldn't think of a single coherent sentence. Her hands reached out imploringly to his broad, silent back before once more dropping to her sides. She'd just have to begin at the beginning.

"When I found out that my father still cared for us as if we were his only family, even when he was married to someone else, it destroyed all the illusions I had lived with for so long. When I was young I thought that people married and lived happily ever after. But our family was different from the others I knew, and I blamed my father. It never dawned on me that both of them could have wanted such an unusual setup. It's only recently that I've grown up enough emotionally to realize that nothing is ever just one person's fault."

Kurt continued to stare out the window, his silence becoming oppressive. "Go on," he requested.

"That's it. I love you, but I was afraid to make a commitment to you for fear of losing you later, like I thought my mother lost my father, like I thought *I* lost my father. Now I realize that if I don't have you, I don't have anything." She took a deep breath, letting it out slowly. "I'm accepting your proposal and I promise to try hard to make our marriage work."

"It sounds like a Girl Scout pledge, Victoria. It's not enough."

"What else do you want, for goodness' sake? Do you want me to jump out the window to prove my love? Do you want me to lie down on your carpet so you can walk all over me? Well, I won't do it!"

"I don't want you to do any of that. I want you to tell me why you love me, why you've suddenly decided that you won't lose yourself in my image." He glanced over his shoulder at her. "Those were the reasons why you were hesitant before, weren't they?"

Anger and frustration were making her adrenaline pump. She closed her eyes and said a quick prayer, hoping that he would be able to read between the lines and understand the feeling her inadequate words were trying to communicate. "I don't know why I love you. It could be because you have such knowing hands, a quick mind, a crooked smile, a giving nature or even a beautiful body. I do know that you have a tendency to read my mind, but this time you don't seem to have any idea what I'm thinking." She waited for a reaction to her teasing, but there was none. "Turn around, Kurt. Look at me," she pleaded. "Don't let me continue to make an absolute fool out of myself if you've decided you can't stand the sight of me anymore."

Kurt did as she asked, his arms still crossed over his broad chest, the expensive dark-brown fabric of his suit jacket stretched across his biceps to accentuate the strength of them. "I haven't decided anything, Victoria. I just don't know if I can cope with you, your moods, your wild whims and fancies. You've been telling me how important your freedom is to you, and suddenly you walk in here to announce that not only is it not important anymore, but you've decided that you want to marry me. What's really odd is that it was all right for you to reject me, but it's not fair for me to do the same to you."

Her eyes pleaded for him to understand. "I know. Women expect all sorts of things from men that aren't right or realistic. Like expecting you to be able to take rejection better than we do, or being brave in the face of adversity."

She walked toward him, her step firm, her eyes locking with his so he could see the truth of her words reflected there. "All I know is that I love you with all my heart, and that that love frightens me. It frightened me so much that I began running away from it even before I realized what it was, and I've been running ever since. But now I can't run anymore. I finally had to stop and face some home truths.

"I've held a grudge, a childish grudge, against my parents for not being able to keep to my picture of what an ideal marriage should be like. I thought that if they loved each other, as they obviously did, then that should solve all their problems. When I finally realized that it didn't, I was crushed. I no longer had faith in any marriage. I only saw the pain, never the joy. I didn't realize that the joy of a marriage is as private as two people make it." She waved her hand in the air, dismissing her findings. "But my parents weren't the core of my problems. *I* was. I blamed everything on my father, on men, and in doing so, I made you take the brunt of my anger.

"But the other night, when you walked out the door and I knew that you wouldn't return, I had to face facts and, in doing that, face myself. I don't want to live without you." Victoria's voice dropped an octave. She placed her hands on the firmness of his chest, her fingertips feeling the strength of the heartbeat beneath. "I want to be near you in all the ways a woman can be near a man. I want to be there at night when you come in, to share a drink and conversation with you. I want to see you leave in the morning, knowing that at odd times during the day a memory of making love to me will flash through your mind. I want to breathe deep of the special scent of you, touch the strength and vitality of your body, hold you close, disappear in your arms to be absorbed inside you. I want to know the corners of your mind and the planes of your body. I want you to need only me as much as I need only you." She hesitated. "I want you to love me as much as I love you, Kurt."

"And what about the power I'm supposed to wield with my money?"

"I don't care."

"And the family you profess to hate?"

"I lied. I love them."

"And the plastic women you'll have to rub elbows with during parties?"

"I'll find something in common with them. After all, they were young once, too." Her hands strayed to his throat, her soothing fingers slowly undoing the knot of his tie. He swallowed deeply, but showed no further reaction.

"And the moped?"

"I'll let you pay the gas bill on my car." She dropped the tie to the floor and began loosening the top button of his shirt.

"Are you going to act sweet, demure and polite? Be a proud figurehead in high society?"

"Yes, yes." Her hands were busily unbuttoning his shirt, and when the last button was undone she began tugging on his belt.

"Liar," he muttered, his hands dangling at his sides, balled into fists.

Her eyes widened, hurt. "You don't believe me?"

He continued to stare at her, his hands clenching and unclenching, his eyes showing as much hurt pride and disillusionment as hers had ever done.

He reached over and flicked the switch on the intercom. "Margie, I don't want to be disturbed under any circumstances. Understand?" he growled.

"Yes, boss. You're out for the day," she confirmed.

Victoria watched him straighten up and face her once more. Her blood pounded through her veins at such a fast rate that she was sure he could hear the noise.

"And now that we know my requirements, and

before I decide if you've answered me truthfully, what are yours for me?"

Her hands knotted in front of her as she stared at him, her confusion plain to see. "I'm not sure what you mean."

"I mean that after giving all those concessions to me, you must want to demand a few of your own. What are they?" His voice was still velvety rough, grating sensuously against her already raw nerves.

"Will you promise to hold me close when I want you to? Just hold me. No questions asked and no advances made."

"Yes."

"Do you promise you won't have any other women in your life?"

"Does that include Margie?"

"Not as long as she remains on the other side of this desk."

"Yes."

She was getting into the spirit of this now, and watching his chocolate eyes turn darker and knowing what was on his mind, she continued, teasing him with her glance. "Do you promise that you won't try to buy me with presents and trips?"

"That's a cheap enough yes," he answered dryly.

"And will you make love to me when I approach you and not be chauvinistic enough to want me only on your terms?"

His voice deepened even more. "That's fair," he answered. "As long as I don't have a headache."

Her hands once more reached for his buckle. "And will you promise to love me the best you know how?"

Her voice was a mere whisper, all her pent-up emotions showing in her face.

He began taking the large wooden hairpins from her hair, letting it cascade over his hands and down her back in long, rolling tendrils. "I promise to know you and to love you, to cherish and protect you. I promise to let you make mistakes, to learn, to grow and to let you love me." His arms finally drew her close to his strong form and he gave a contented sigh as he buried his face in the cloud of hair at her neck. "And if you ever put me through this again I promise I will beat you within an inch of your life."

"Male chauvinist!" she chortled.

"You bet," he retorted. "And to prove it, I'm ordering you downstairs to *Newstime*'s clinic so they can do a blood test, then I want you with me in the morning so we can apply for a license. I'm not letting you out of my sight until you marry me."

"If that's supposed to be a form of punishment, you've got a new slant on it!" she chuckled, finally sliding his shirt aside so she could inhale the male scent of his skin. "But I'll go for it. My mother didn't raise no dummy."

His hands tightened on her waist. "No, but she made sure you didn't grow up in time for any man to break down your barriers . . . until me. And for that I'm eternally grateful."

Then the door was locked, the curtains drawn and all talking stopped. Mr. Kurt Morgan and his bride-to-be were very busy being very untraditional . . . making love in the middle of the day.

# Silhouette Desire
# 15-Day Trial Offer

## A new romance series that explores contemporary relationships in exciting detail

**Six Silhouette Desire romances, free for 15 days!**
We'll send you six new Silhouette Desire romances
to look over for 15 days, absolutely free! If you decide
not to keep the books, return them and owe nothing.

**Six books a month, free home delivery.** If you like
Silhouette Desire romances as much as we think you
will, keep them and return your payment with the
invoice. Then we will send you six new books every
month to preview, just as soon as they are published.
You pay only for the books you decide to keep, and
you never pay postage and handling.

# YOU'LL BE SWEPT AWAY
# WITH SILHOUETTE DESIRE

## $1.75 each

1 ☐ CORPORATE AFFAIR
James

2 ☐ LOVE'S SILVER WEB
Monet

3 ☐ WISE FOLLY
Clay

4 ☐ KISS AND TELL
Carey

5 ☐ WHEN LAST WE LOVED
Baker

6 ☐ A FRENCHMAN'S KISS
Mallory

7 ☐ NOT EVEN FOR LOVE
St. Claire

8 ☐ MAKE NO PROMISES
Dee

9 ☐ MOMENT IN TIME
Simms

10 ☐ WHENEVER I LOVE YOU
Smith

## $1.95 each

11 ☐ VELVET TOUCH
James

12 ☐ THE COWBOY AND THE
LADY  Palmer

13 ☐ COME BACK, MY LOVE
Wallace

14 ☐ BLANKET OF STARS
Valley

15 ☐ SWEET BONDAGE
Vernon

16 ☐ DREAM COME TRUE
Major

17 ☐ OF PASSION BORN
Simms

18 ☐ SECOND HARVEST
Ross

19 ☐ LOVER IN PURSUIT
James

20 ☐ KING OF DIAMONDS
Allison

21 ☐ LOVE INTHE CHINA SEA
Baker

22 ☐ BITTERSWEET IN BERN
Durant

23 ☐ CONSTANT STRANGER
Sunshine

24 ☐ SHARED MOMENTS
Baxter

25 ☐ RENAISSANCE MAN
James

26 ☐ SEPTEMBER MORNING
Palmer

27 ☐ ON WINGS OF NIGHT
Conrad

28 ☐ PASSIONATE JOURNEY
Lovan

29 ☐ ENCHANTED DESERT
Michelle

30 ☐ PAST FORGETTING
Lind

31 ☐ RECKLESS PASSION
James

32 ☐ YESTERDAY'S DREAMS
Clay

Silhouette Desire

# Silhouette Desire

## Coming Next Month

### Affair Of Honor by Stephanie James

When Ryder Sterne held her in his embrace, Philosophy professor Brenna Llewellyn almost forgot why she was at the mountain retreat, and soon found herself abandoning all logic for love.

### Friends And Lovers by Diana Palmer

They were close friends, but now Madeline found that John's touch was somehow different. It ignited a passion in her that led them to discover a whole new closeness.

### Shadow Of The Mountain by Pamela Lind

Deke Jordan had rights and could lay equal claim to Shelley Grant's small mining company. But Shelley didn't expect him to stake a claim on her with kisses she fought—but couldn't resist.

### Embers Of The Sun by Raye Morgan

Artist Charla Evans came to Japan to study raku pottery—and to escape an unhappy love. But then she met tycoon Stephen Conners and realized she couldn't live for art alone!

### Winter Lady by Janet Joyce

America's heartthrob Devlin Paige saved Raine Morgan when he rescued her on the ski slopes in Minnesota's desolate hills . . . but he left Raine burning with a reckless passion she couldn't escape.

### If Ever You Need Me by Paula Fulford

When Julia Somers stepped off the stage in triumph, producer Roy Allison offered her a star-making role . . . and more. But could love be real in his celluloid world?